Teaching
comprehension
strategies

Developing reading comprehension skills

Model

Practice

Apply

Understanding words

Identifying the main idea

Finding information

Sequencing

Finding similarities and differences

Predicting

Concluding

Summarising

Inferring

Cause and effect

Fact or opinion

Point of view and purpose

Prim-Ed Publishing

TEACHING COMPREHENSION STRATEGIES *(Book A)*

Published by Prim-Ed Publishing 2007
Reprinted Prim-Ed Publishing 2014
Copyright© R.I.C. Publications® 2006
ISBN 978-1-84654-117-9
PR–6296

Additional titles available in this series:
TEACHING COMPREHENSION STRATEGIES *(Book B)*
TEACHING COMPREHENSION STRATEGIES *(Book C)*
TEACHING COMPREHENSION STRATEGIES *(Book D)*
TEACHING COMPREHENSION STRATEGIES *(Book E)*
TEACHING COMPREHENSION STRATEGIES *(Book F)*
TEACHING COMPREHENSION STRATEGIES *(Book G)*

Internet websites
In some cases, websites or specific URLs may be recommended. While these are checked and rechecked at the time of publication, the publisher has no control over any subsequent changes which may be made to webpages. It is *strongly* recommended that the class teacher checks *all* URLs before allowing pupils to access them.

View all pages online   **Website:** www.prim-ed.com

Foreword

Teaching comprehension strategies is a series of seven books using modelling, discussion and guided and independent practice to teach pupils strategies they can use to develop different reading comprehension skills.

Titles in this series include:

- *Teaching comprehension strategies—Book A*
- *Teaching comprehension strategies—Book B*
- *Teaching comprehension strategies—Book C*
- *Teaching comprehension strategies—Book D*
- *Teaching comprehension strategies—Book E*
- *Teaching comprehension strategies—Book F*
- *Teaching comprehension strategies—Book G*

Each book in this series is also provided in digital format on the accompanying CD.

Contents

Teachers notes

What is comprehension?

Comprehension is a cognitive process. It involves the capacity of the mind to understand, using logic and reasoning. It is not, as some pupils sadly believe, trying to guess the answers to formal exercises, done with a pencil and paper, after reading text. Pupils need to know **how to think about and make decisions about a text after reading it**.

Teaching comprehension

Comprehension skills can and should be developed by teaching pupils strategies that are appropriate to a particular comprehension skill and then providing opportunities for them to discuss and practise applying those strategies to the texts they read. These strategies can be a series of clearly defined steps to follow.

Pupils need to understand that it is the **process** not the product that is more important. In other words, they need to understand **how** it is done before they are required to demonstrate that they can do it.

Higher order comprehension skills are within the capacity of very young pupils, but care needs to be taken to ensure that the text is at an appropriate level and that the language of discussion is also age-appropriate.

The text can be read to the pupils. The emphasis should be on discussion and the comprehension activities should be completed orally before moving to supported and then independent pencil and paper work.

Note: Some pupils may not be able to complete the activities independently.

Pupils completing the activities in this book will need to become aware of the concepts of paragraphs and verses. (Pupils should discuss the numbering of the paragraphs or verses in texts before commencing the activities.)

They should practise saying and reading words such as 'strategies', 'paragraphs', 'sentence' etc. so they are familiar with them.

Note: The terms *skills* and *strategies* are sometimes confused. The following explanation provides some clarification of how the two terms are used in this book.

Skills relate to competent performance and come from knowledge, practice and aptitude.

Strategies involve planning and tactics.

In other words, we can teach *strategies* that will help pupils to acquire specific comprehension *skills*.

Metacognitive strategies

Metacognitive strategies, teaching pupils how to think about thinking, are utilised in developing the twelve comprehension skills taught in this book. Metacognitive strategies are modelled and explained to pupils for each skill. As this is essentially an oral process, teachers are encouraged to elaborate on and discuss the explanations provided on the 'Learning about the skill' pages and to talk about different thought processes they would use in answering each question.

Pupils will require different levels of support before they are able to work independently to comprehend, make decisions about text and choose the best answer in multiple choice questions. This support includes modelling the metacognitive processes, as well as supported practice with some hints and clues provided.

Comprehension strategies

The exercises in this book have been written not to test, but to stimulate and challenge pupils and to help them to develop their thinking processes through modelled metacognitive strategies, discussion and guided and independent practice. There are no trick questions, but there are many that require and encourage pupils to use logic and reasoning.

Particularly in the higher order comprehension skills, there may be more than one acceptable answer. The reader's prior knowledge and experience will influence some of his or her decisions about the text. Teachers may choose to accept an answer if a pupil can justify and explain his or her choice. Therefore, some of the answers provided should not be considered prescriptive but more a guide and a basis for discussion.

There are pupils with excellent cognitive processing skills and a particular aptitude for and interest in reading who develop advanced reading comprehension skills independently. However, for the majority of pupils, the strategies they need to develop and demonstrate comprehension need to be made explicit and carefully taught, not just tested; the rationale behind this series of books.

Teachers notes

The following twelve comprehension skills are included in this book.

Understanding words	Sequencing	Concluding	Cause and effect
Finding information	Finding similarities and differences	Summarising	Fact or opinion
Identifying the main idea	Predicting	Inferring	Point of view and purpose

These twelve skills have been divided into four sections, each with teachers notes, three different comprehension skills and three pupil assessment tests.

Each group of six pages given to a particular skill consists of:

- Pupil page 1   – Text 1
- Pupil page 2   – Learning about the skill (teacher modelling of the skill)
- Pupil page 3   – Practice page (pupil practice with teacher assistance)
- Pupil page 4   – On your own (independent pupil activity)
- Pupil page 5   – Text 2
- Pupil page 6   – Try it out (independent pupil activity with one clue)

There is a test at the end of each section to assess the three skills, consisting of:

- Pupil page 1 – Text 3
- Pupil page 2 – Skill 1 test
- Pupil page 3 – Skill 2 test
- Pupil page 4 – Skill 3 test

A class test record sheet is provided on page viii and an individual pupil evaluation page is on page ix.

There are a variety of different text types used and identified in this book including:

Reports	Narratives	Discussions
Recounts	Procedures	Explanations

Teachers pages

The three skills in the section are identified.

Background information about the skill and teaching strategies is provided.

An objective states the expected outcome.

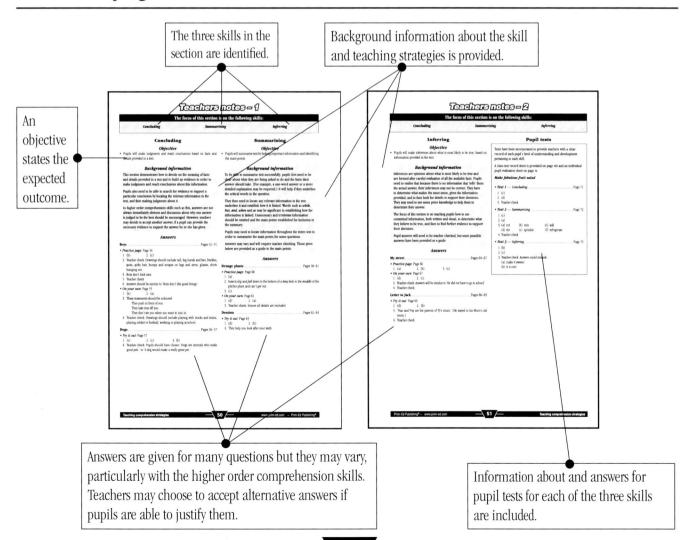

Answers are given for many questions but they may vary, particularly with the higher order comprehension skills. Teachers may choose to accept alternative answers if pupils are able to justify them.

Information about and answers for pupil tests for each of the three skills are included.

Pupil pages

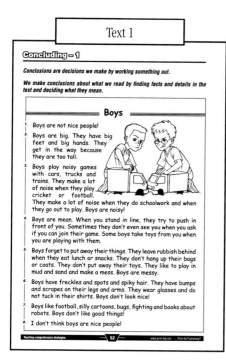

Text 1

- The skill is identified and defined.
- The text is presented.

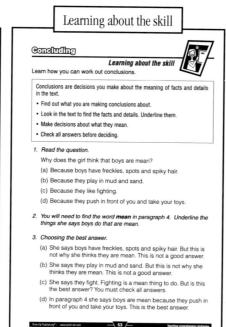

Learning about the skill

- The logo indicates that this is a teaching page.
- Steps and strategies are outlined.
- Multiple choice questions are presented and metacognitive processes for choosing the best answer are described.

Practice page

- The logo indicates that this is a teacher and pupil page.
- Some multiple choice questions and others requiring explanations are presented with prompts or clues to assist pupils.

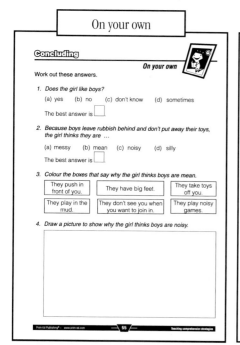

On your own

- The logo indicates that this is a pupil page.
- At least one multiple choice question and others requiring explanation are presented for pupils to complete.

Text 2

- The skill is identified.
- The text is presented.

Try it out

- The logo indicates that this is a pupil page.
- Multiple choice questions and some requiring explanation are included.

Pupil test pages

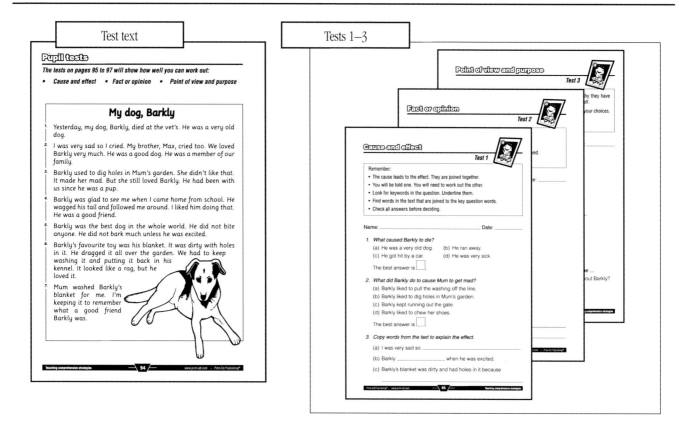

- The three skills to be tested are identified.
- The text is presented.

- Logo to indicate that this is a pupil page.
- The comprehension skill to be tested is identified and appropriate strategies and steps revised.
- Multiple choice questions and others requiring more explanation are presented.

Curriculum links

Country	Subject	Level	Objective
England	English	Year 1	• Draw on what they already know or on background information and vocabulary provided by the teacher. • Check that the text makes sense to them as they read and correct inaccurate reading. • Discuss the significance of the title and events. • Make inferences on the basis of what is being said and done. • Predict what might happen on the basis of what has been read so far.
Northern Ireland	Language and Literacy	Year 2	• Read a range of texts with some independence. • Sequence stories. • Read and follow simple instructions. • Use extended vocabulary when discussing text and retelling stories. • Make and give reasons for predictions.
Republic of Ireland	English	Senior Infants	• Recall and talk about significant events and details in stories. • Predict future incidents and outcomes in stories.
Scotland	English	A	• Build up confidence in handling information and answering questions. • Share and discuss texts; e.g. questioning, predicting what might happen next and picking out important ideas.
Scotland	English	B	• Use fiction and nonfiction texts. • Complete activities encouraging discussion, prediction, answering pertinent questions, use of contextual clues and sequencing.
Wales	English	KS 1	• Read literature covering a range of categories. • Understand and respond to stories and poems; e.g. talk about characters/events/language, say what might happen next in a story and retell stories.

Comprehension skills class test record

Name	Understanding words	Finding information	Identifying the main idea	Sequencing	Finding similarities and differences	Predicting	Concluding	Summarising	Inferring	Cause and effect	Fact or opinion	Point of view and purpose	Notes

Individual pupil evaluation

Name:_____

Skill	Strategies			Comments
Understanding words	knowledge	😊 ———————— ☹		
	application	😊 ———————— ☹		
Finding information	knowledge	😊 ———————— ☹		
	application	😊 ———————— ☹		
Identifying the main idea	knowledge	😊 ———————— ☹		
	application	😊 ———————— ☹		
Sequencing	knowledge	😊 ———————— ☹		
	application	😊 ———————— ☹		
Finding similarities and differences	knowledge	😊 ———————— ☹		
	application	😊 ———————— ☹		
Predicting	knowledge	😊 ———————— ☹		
	application	😊 ———————— ☹		
Concluding	knowledge	😊 ———————— ☹		
	application	😊 ———————— ☹		
Summarising	knowledge	😊 ———————— ☹		
	application	😊 ———————— ☹		
Inferring	knowledge	😊 ———————— ☹		
	application	😊 ———————— ☹		
Cause and effect	knowledge	😊 ———————— ☹		
	application	😊 ———————— ☹		
Fact or opinion	knowledge	😊 ———————— ☹		
	application	😊 ———————— ☹		
Point of view and purpose	knowledge	😊 ———————— ☹		
	application	😊 ———————— ☹		

The focus of this section is on the following skills:

Understanding words	*Finding information*	*Identifying the main idea*

Understanding words

Objectives

- Pupils will use contextual information to determine the meaning of words and phrases in texts.
- Pupils will apply metacognitive strategies to reflect on how they determined the meaning of words and phrases.

Background information

The meaning of the words and phrases we use depends on how they are used in a sentence. Contextual information is a very useful cue in determining meaning.

Some pupils find the concept difficult and need explicit modelling and supported practice to understand this and to use contextual information to determine word or phrase meaning. Many are unaware they can determine meaning by careful consideration of the text and that there are clues there to help them.

In choosing answers to multiple choice questions, pupils should first locate the word in the text. They should then read the sentence and perhaps some others around it, as well as any other parts of the text that may provide clues to its meaning. They should consider all answers before making a decision and choosing one.

Pupils may also need to use syntactic information to check that the meaning they have selected 'fits' the sentence.

Answers

The farm trip..Pages 4 –7

- *Practice page*: Page 6
  1. (a)   2. (b)
  3. (a) a label you wear to tell who you are
     (b) cream to stop you from getting sunburnt
- *On your own*: Page 7
  1. (a)   2. (d)   3. (c)
  4. Teacher check
  5. Teacher check

Teeth for Tex Rex ....Pages 8 –9

- *Try it out*: Page 9
  1. (b)   2. (a)   3. (d)
  4. (a) devour — eat
     (b) prickly — bumpy, spiky
     (c) gums — where your teeth grow
     (d) whispered — spoke softly

Finding information

Objectives

- Pupils scan text to locate keywords.
- Pupils read text carefully, as many times as necessary to find important and supporting information and details.

Background information

This section models and explains how to locate keywords in questions and then in the text. Pupils are encouraged to scan a text to identify keywords and then to read the text a number of times, if necessary, to locate details and to determine which details are important in clarifying information and in supporting their ideas and the choices they have made.

Many pupils are unaware of the need to return to text or even that this is permitted and believe they should have understood and remembered all details from their first reading.

Having identified the keyword in a question, some pupils find it quite difficult to scan text to locate these words. It is suggested that they are assisted by being given additional information; for example, the specific paragraph they need to read. Many may not be aware that the first sentence in a paragraph often tells what that particular paragraph is about and reading it quickly can be very helpful.

When locating details in informational text, particular care should be taken to ensure that the information is accurate and that it is recorded correctly. Although there is generally more room for interpretation in fiction, this skill requires pupils to locate information that is stated in the text.

Answers

Teddy bears ....Pages 10 –13

- *Practice page*: Page 12
  1. (a)   2. (c)
  3. two arms, two legs, nose, two ears, eyes
- *On your own*: Page 13
  1. (d)   2. (b)
  3. to comfort sick or sad children, to be friends with lonely children, for collecting and displaying
  4. Paddington Bear, Winnie the Pooh/Teacher check

Fruit roll ....Pages 14–15

- *Try it out*: Page 15
  1. (c)   2. (b)
  3. (a) paper towel   (b) 10 seconds   (c) peanut butter and jam
     (d) banana   (e) tortilla
  4. Eat and enjoy!

The focus of this section is on the following skills:

Understanding words   *Finding information*   *Identifying the main idea*

Identifying the main idea

Objective

• Pupils determine the main idea in a text and in specific paragraphs.

Background information

If pupils are able to identify the main idea of a text they are more likely to comprehend it. This section models how this is done. It provides opportunities for pupils to practise this skill and to understand why it is important.

The main idea connects the ideas expressed in the paragraphs and gives coherence to the text. Some pupils may find it easier to practise this skill at the paragraph level, particularly if they understand that the first sentence is often the topic sentence and may contain the main idea.

Another very significant clue is the title, which usually indicates what the text is about and may incorporate its main idea. Another is the conclusion, which in some text types often restates the main idea. In discussion text, the main idea is stated in the first paragraph, where the writer is expected to state the issue and his or her position on it.

When selecting the main idea in multiple choice questions, it is essential that pupils read **all** the choices carefully, because while all of them are often ideas expressed in the text, generally one is more of an overall summary of the text's focus.

Answers

Tree house ....Pages 16–19

• *Practice page*: Page 18
  1. (b)   2. (c)   3. (c)   4. (a)
• *On your own*: Page 19
  1. (d)   2. (a)
  3. Teacher check (Pupils should have drawn a tree house in the garden with a railing, cushions, blankets and toys.)
  4. Teacher check

My favourite top... Pages 20 –21

• *Try it out*: Page 21
  1. (d)   2. (a)
  3. Teacher check (Aunt Judy uses a fancy machine which puts special pictures on the things she makes.)
  4. Teacher check

Pupil tests

Tests have been incorporated to provide teachers with a clear record of each pupil's level of understanding and development pertaining to each skill.

A class test record sheet is provided on page viii and an individual pupil evaluation sheet on page ix.

Helping at home
(NOTE: Pages 22 to 25 are designed to be used in conjunction with each other.)

• **Test 1** — *Understanding words* .... Page 23
  1. (d)
  2. (b)
  3. (a) can get thing done (b)   get more exercise

• **Test 2** — *Finding information* .... Page 24
  1. (c)
  2. Teacher check (Answers should include picking up toys, taking out rubbish, dressing themselves, getting their own cereal for breakfast.)
  3. important members of the family.

• **Test 3** — *Identifying the main idea* .... Page 25
  1. (b)
  2. (a) paragraph 2
     (b) paragraph 3
     (c) paragraph 4
     (d) paragraph 5
     (e) paragraph 6

We use words to tell other people things. We need to understand what words mean. We also need to know some ways to work out what new words mean.

The farm trip

1. On Friday, everyone in our class got on a bus and went to visit a farm to learn more about farm animals. We took some parents to help Mrs White look after us.

2. Our lunches and snacks were in plastic bags with our names written on labels. They went in a coloured plastic box in a secret place in the bottom of the bus. My mum put a small bottle of sunscreen in my lunch bag so I could spread it on and not get sunburnt.

3. We all wore our school uniform and name badges in case we got lost.

4. It took a very long time to travel there. The big bus was noisy and uncomfortable because we had to travel down windy countryside roads with holes in them.

5. When we finally arrived at the farm, we got into small groups and wandered around looking at and touching all the animals.

6. By the time we got on the bus to go back to school we were all exhausted. Some children even fell asleep! We all had great fun!

Learning about the skill

Learn how to work out the meaning of new words.

- Find the word. Draw a line under it.

- Find the sentence the word is in. Think about the other words in the sentence because they may help.

- If you still don't know, think about the sentences before and after, and even the whole paragraph if you need to.

- Check all the answers before choosing.

---

1. *Read the question.*

   What does the word **parents** mean?

   (a) a fruit   (b) to run

   (c) pets   (d) mums and dads

2. *Draw a line under the word **parents** in paragraph 1.*

3. *Choosing the best answer.*

   (a) The sentence tells about something or someone who is going to help Mrs White look after the children. A fruit couldn't do this! This is not a good answer.

   (b) If we put the words **to run** in the sentence in place of **parents**, the sentence would say 'We took some **to run** to help Mrs White look after us'. This makes the sentence sound wrong. This is not a good answer.

   (c) **Pets** would not be able to help Mrs White look after the children. This is not a good answer.

   (d) If we put the words **mums and dads** in the sentence instead of **parents** it makes sense, because mums and dads would be able to help Mrs White look after the children. This is the best answer.

Practice page

Practise working out the meaning of words.
(Clues are given to help you!)

1. Find and draw a line under the word **labels** in paragraph 2.

   Does it mean:

   (a) bits of paper stuck on?

   (b) food?   (c) sticky?   (d) jump?

   I think the best answer is ☐.

   > **Think!**
   > Try each answer in the sentence. See which one makes the most sense.

2. Find and draw a line under the word **snacks** in paragraph 2.

   Does it mean:

   (a) to creep?   (b) food and drink?

   (c) happy?   (d) clowns?

   I think the best answer is ☐.

   > **Think!**
   > The sentence will give you a clue.

3. Circle the best answer.

   (a) **Badges** (paragraph 3) are ...

   - animals who build burrows

   - a label you wear to tell who you are

   - kinds of trees   • homes

   > **Think!**
   > The word before **badges** tells you what they are used for.

   (b) **Sunscreen** (paragraph 2) means ...

   - ants   • yell

   - cream to stop you from getting sunburnt

   - a place to hang wet clothes

   > **Think!**
   > The sentence will give you a clue about what it is used for.

Understanding words

Work out the meanings of these words and phrases.

1. *Draw a line under the words* **to travel.** *(Paragraph 4)*

   Do they mean:

   (a) to go somewhere? (b) to hit?

   (c) painted?   (d) to cry?   The best meaning is ☐.

2. *Draw a line under the word* **uncomfortable.** *(Paragraph 4)*

   Does it mean:

   (a) not pretty?   (b) running?

   (c) ten?   (d) bouncy?   The best meaning is ☐.

3. *Draw a line under the word* **wandered.** *(Paragraph 5)*

   Does it mean:

   (a) a magic object?   (b) head?

   (c) walked around?   (d) to think?   The best meaning is ☐.

4. *Draw a picture to show what* **exhausted** *means. (Paragraph 6)*

5. *Circle the best word.*

   The title **The farm trip** is a good one. | Yes   No |

Teeth for Tex Rex

1. A very long time ago in a bushy forest, Tex Rex, a very big baby dinosaur, lived with his mum, Mex Rex, and his dad, Lex Rex.

2. Tex Rex was very unhappy. His friends, Hex and Wex, had both grown lots of sharp, pointed teeth while he was still waiting for his first tooth to appear.

3. All T-rex dinosaurs had giant, pointed teeth which they used to devour other dinosaurs for dinner. He wanted to be just like everyone else. He was supposed to be one of the scariest reptiles who ever lived, but instead he was frightened and shy.

4. He filled his mouth with lots of small, sharp, pointy rocks, but the rocks fell out when he tried to roar.

5. He chewed prickly plants to make it easy for his teeth to come through his gums. He still didn't have any teeth!

6. One night, he saw a star falling from the sky. 'Wish I may! Wish I might, have the wish, I wish tonight!' he whispered to himself as he lay down to sleep.

7. As the sun came up the next morning, Tex Rex yawned and opened his mouth very wide.

8. 'Oh look, Tex Rex', said his mum. 'What a lovely shiny, pointy, sharp tooth you have!'

Understanding words

Try it out

Use the strategies you learnt and practised in
The farm trip to work out the meaning of the words.

> Remember: Find the words, read the words around them and think!

1. **What does the word *forest* mean? (Paragraph 1)**

    (a) four   (b) a place with lots of trees

    (c) wet   (d) before everyone else

    The best answer is ☐.

    > **Think!**
    > The dinosaurs lived there.

2. **What does *to appear* mean? (Paragraph 2)**

    (a) to be seen   (b) on top   (c) to jump   (d) to eat

    The best answer is ☐.

3. **Tick the correct box. A *reptile* (paragraph 3) is ...**

    (a) a race   ☐   (b) something in a house   ☐

    (c) a person   ☐   (d) an animal   ☐

4. **Draw a line from each word to its meaning.**

    (a) devour (paragraph 3)   •   • where your teeth grow

    (b) prickly (paragraph 5)   •   • eat

    (c) gums (paragraph 5)   •   • spoke softly

    (d) whispered (paragraph 6) •   • bumpy, spiky

When you read you can usually remember some things. If you are asked questions, you should read the text again to find information and check that you are correct.

Remember: The answer you are looking for is there, you just need to find it!

Teddy bears

1. Teddy bears are stuffed toy bears.

2. Teddy bears have soft fur on their bodies. They have two arms and two legs. They have a big, black squashed nose and two small ears that stand up. They usually have big brown eyes.

3. Teddy bears can help sick or sad children feel better. They make good friends for lonely children.

4. Teddy bears come in different sizes and colours. Many are dressed in cute costumes.

5. Teddy bears were named after an American president called Theodore Roosevelt. His nickname was 'Teddy'.

6. Some adults like to collect teddy bears to display. Some of these teddy bears can be very expensive.

7. Two well-known teddy bears in stories are Paddington Bear and Winnie the Pooh.

8. Teddy bears are great toys for anyone to own.

Learning about the skill

Learn how to find information.

- Read the question very carefully. Keywords will tell you what information and details you need to find.

- Underline the keywords in the question.

- Think about an answer—but you must look at the text again to check that you are correct.

- Find the keywords in the text. Carefully read the information around them.

- Check all the answers before choosing one.

---

1. *Read the question.*

   What are teddy bears?

   (a) Teddy bears are wind-up toys.

   (b) Teddy bears are real animals.

   (c) Teddy bears are stuffed toy bears.

   (d) Teddy bears are plants.

2. *The keywords are **what** and **teddy bears.** Underline them in the question.*

3. *Choosing the best answer.*

   (a) Teddy bears are toys but not wind-up toys. This is not the best answer.

   (b) Teddy bears are toys and are not real. This is not a good answer.

   (d) Teddy bears are not plants. This is a very bad answer.

   (c) The first sentence says that teddy bears are stuffed toy bears. This is the best answer.

Practice page

Practise finding information. (Clues are given to help you.)

1. What are the bodies of teddy bears covered with?

    (a) Teddy bears have soft fur on their bodies.

    (b) Teddy bears have scales.

    (c) Teddy bears have hair.

    (d) Teddy bears have spikes.

    I think the best answer is ☐.

    Think!
    Find the exact words in paragraph 2.

2. Where did the name 'teddy bear' come from? Circle the correct answer.

    (a) Teddy bears are named after a town.

    (b) Teddy bears are named after Mr Ted.

    (c) Teddy bears are named after a man whose nickname was 'Teddy'.

    (d) Teddy bears are named after a bear in a book.

    Think!
    Read paragraph 5.

3. Write a list of body parts all teddy bears should have.

    Think!
    Find a paragraph which lists all the body parts.

Finding information

Work out these answers.

1. *What colour are teddy bears' noses? (Paragraph 2)*

    (a) red   (b) blue   (c) brown   (d) black

    The best answer is ☐.

2. *What can be different about teddy bears? (Paragraph 4)*

    (a) the number of arms and legs   (b) their size and colour

    (c) the number of noses   (d) the number of eyes

    The best answer is ☐.

3. *Write two things that teddy bears are used for. (Paragraphs 3 and 6)*

    (a) _____

    _____

    (b) _____

    _____

4. *Write about or draw two well-known teddy bears. (Paragraph 7)*

Fruit roll

You will need:

- 1 small flour tortilla
- 2 teaspoons jam
- paper towel
- teaspoon
- 2 teaspoons peanut butter
- 1 peeled banana
- knife
- microwave oven

Steps:

(a) Put tortilla on paper towel.

(b) Microwave for 10 seconds.

(c) Spread with peanut butter.

(d) Add jam on top.

(e) Put banana near edge of tortilla.

(f) Roll up tortilla.

Test:

Eat and enjoy!

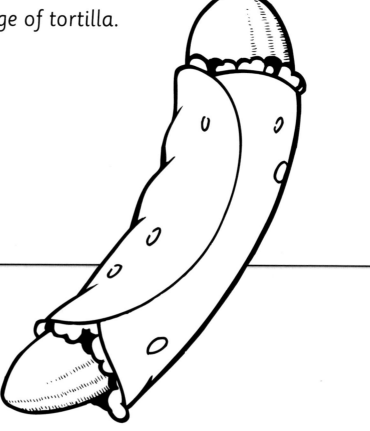

Finding information

Use the strategies you learnt and practised in
Teddy bears.

> Remember:
>
> • Find the keywords in the questions and the text.
>
> • Check all answers before choosing one.

1. *How many* **things** *do you need to make fruit rolls?*

   (a) 4   (b) 6   (c) 8   (d) 5

   Think!
   Count everything you need! Not just the ingredients!

   The best answer is ☐.

2. *What two spreads are used?*

   (a) honey and jam   (b) peanut butter and jam

   (c) peanut butter and honey   (d) honey and cheese

   The best answer is ☐.

3. *Complete the sentences about the* **steps**.

   (a) The tortilla is placed on _____.

   (b) The tortilla is microwaved for _____.

   (c) The tortilla is spread with _____

   and _____.

   (d) The _____ is placed near the
   edge of the tortilla.

   (e) Roll up the _____.

4. *How can you* **test** *the recipe?* _____

If you know what the main idea of a text is, you will have a much better chance of understanding it.

TREE HOUSE

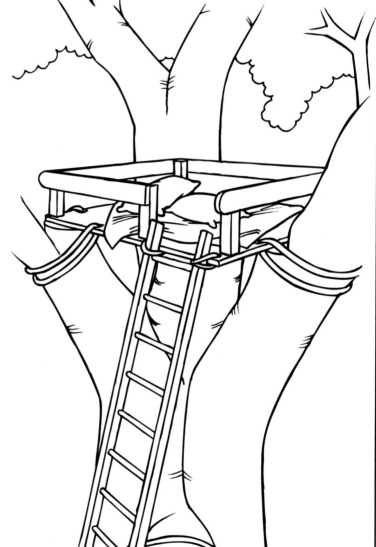

1. This is how we built a tree house in the big tree in our back garden.

2. Mum and Dad helped us build it with scraps of wood and junk. We found lots of junk we could use in the shed.

3. We tied rope to an old ladder. Then we tied the ladder to the trunk of the tree.

4. We used a big flat piece of wood for a floor in the fork of the tree. Then we used more rope and nails to fix the floor to the tree.

5. We made a railing on the sides to stop us from falling out. We used bits of an old fence.

6. Finally, we placed soft cushions and blankets in the tree house for us to sit on.

7. Mark, Karl, Kim and I had great fun building and playing in our tree house. Even our toys had fun!

Identifying the main idea

Learning about the skill

Learn how to work out the main idea and why it is important.

There are often many ideas but there is one idea that joins the other ideas together. This is the main idea.

- Read the text then ask yourself, what is it mainly about? (The title is a very good clue to the main idea because a good title often tells the reader what the text is about.)

- Always check all the answers before choosing one.

---

1. *Read what you need to find out.*

   The main idea of *Tree house* is:

   (a) about a book

   (b) about a family

   (c) how nice trees look in the garden

   (d) how a tree house can be made

2. *Choosing the best answer.*

   (a) The text is not about books. This is not a good answer.

   (b) The names of some people are given in the text. This is a little idea and not the main idea. This is not a good answer.

   (c) The text tells about trees and gardens but only a little bit. The text does not tell how nice trees look in the garden. This could be an answer but not the best one.

   (d) The text gives lots of steps to explain how a tree house was made. This is the best answer.

Identifying the main idea

Practise finding the main idea. (Clues are given to help you!)

1. Paragraph 1 is mainly about:

   (a) playing in the garden

   (b) where the tree house was built

   (c) trees are homes for birds

   (d) plants are nice to look at

   The best answer is ☐.

   > **Think!**
   > Read paragraph 1 a few times. What do the words tell about?

2. Which paragraph tells what they used to get up into the tree? Draw a line under the correct answer.

   (a) Paragraph 1   (b) Paragraph 2

   (c) Paragraph 3   (d) Paragraph 4

   > **Think!**
   > Look for the name of something which is used for climbing.

3. Draw a line under the correct answer. The main idea of paragraph 2 is:

   (a) Dinner is ready.

   (b) Mum and Dad are good parents.

   (c) About finding junk material for the tree house.

   (d) The tree house is cosy.

   > **Think!**
   > Think about the answers then read the paragraph again.

4. Which paragraph tells how to put a floor in the tree house? Circle the correct answer.

   (a) Paragraph 4   (b) Paragraph 6

   (c) Paragraph 5   (d) Paragraph 2

   > **Think!**
   > Look for the word 'floor'.

Identifying the main idea

Work out these answers.

1. *What is the main idea of paragraph 6?*

    (a) It is fun to have a tree house.

    (b) Tree houses can be big.

    (c) A lot of people can fit in a tree house.

    (d) We made the tree house comfortable.

    The best answer is ☐.

2. *Draw a line under the correct answer about paragraph 5.*

    (a) The tree house had a railing to keep the children safe.

    (b) Fences are useful.

    (c) Trains go on railway tracks.

    (d) The tree house had a roof.

3. *Draw a tree house in a garden. Put in the three main ideas from paragraphs 5, 6 and 7.*

4. *Titles help to tell about the main idea of a text. Is the title* Tree house *a good clue? Circle the correct word.*

Yes	No

My favourite top

1. Aunt Judy made me a blue top for my birthday last year.

2. My blue top has long sleeves and a high neck. The cuffs and collar are dark blue. Blue is my favourite colour. It matches my dark blue tracksuit trousers.

3. We live in a place where it is very cold in winter. Sometimes it snows. We need to wear lots of clothes to keep warm. The blue top is made from thick, fluffy material. It helps me to keep warm.

4. Aunt Judy sews very well. She is always making something for someone. Everyone likes to get something made by Aunt Judy. She makes each thing different and special.

5. Uncle Hank bought Aunt Judy a fancy sewing machine. The sewing machine draws pictures on the clothes she makes. I like aeroplanes so Aunt Judy sewed a coloured aeroplane on my top.

6. I love wearing my favourite blue top. I wonder what Aunt Judy will make for me next year?

Identifying the main idea

Use the strategies you learnt and practised in *Tree house*.

Remember:

- The information is usually in the text.

- Ask yourself 'Which answer tells what it is mainly about?'

- Look at the title too!

- Read all the answers carefully before deciding.

1. *Draw a line under the main idea of paragraph 3.*

    (a) The top keeps the writer cool.

    (b) The top is pretty.

    (c) The top was a birthday present.

    (d) The top keeps the writer warm.

Think!
Make sure that you are looking in paragraph 3!

2. *Circle the main idea of paragraph 4.*

    (a) Everyone likes what Aunt Judy makes them because she sews very well.

    (b) Aunt Judy does not sew well.

    (c) Aunt Judy is old and grumpy.

    (d) Aunt Judy makes all her own clothes.

3. *Write words to tell the main idea of paragraph 5.*

    _____

    _____

4. *Circle yes or no.*

    The title tells the main idea of the whole text.

Yes	No

The tests on pages 23 to 25 will show how well you can:

- *Understand words*
- *Find information*
- *Identify the main idea*

Helping at home

1. Doing jobs at home is good for children. I think all children should have some jobs to do at home.

2. Parents are very busy. Lots of families have mums and dads who work. Children can help by doing jobs. This helps everyone in the family.

3. Children are little but they can help by picking up their toys, taking out the rubbish, dressing themselves and getting their own cereal for breakfast. This helps because adults don't have to do them as well as the bigger jobs.

4. Doing jobs at home teaches children to be responsible. They learn to take charge of the things they have to do. Doing jobs helps children to grow up to be responsible adults.

5. When children do jobs to help, they are being useful. It reminds them that they are important members of the family. It makes them feel good about themselves.

6. Doing jobs can be fun and good exercise too! When children are putting away toys or helping to wash the car, they are exercising. Doing jobs helps children to be more active.

7. Doing jobs at home is good for everyone. I think all children should help at home.

Understanding words

Remember:

- Find the word. Draw a line under it.

- Read the sentence with the word or phrase in it and the ones around it.

- Say the answer word in the sentence to see if it makes sense.

- Check all possible answers before choosing one.

Name: _____ Date: _____

1. *What does the word **adults** mean? (Paragraph 3)*

   (a) animals   (b) two   (c) quiet   (d) grown-ups

   The best meaning is ☐.

2. *What does the word **cereal** mean? (Paragraph 3)*

   (a) look at   (b) food usually eaten in a bowl

   (c) toy   (d) main meal at night

   The best meaning is ☐.

3. *Circle the correct answer.*

   (a) **responsible** (paragraph 4) means:

   - do again   • red

   - good   • can get things done

   (b) **be more active** (paragraph 6) means:

   - get more exercise   • be busy

   - be in a play   • grow

Remember:

- Look in the text to find information.

- Draw a line under keywords in the *question*. This tells what information you are looking for.

- Draw a line under keywords in the *text*. Carefully read information about them.

- Check *all* answers before choosing one.

Name: _____ Date: _____

1. *Why should children **help parents**? (Paragraph 2)*
   (a) Parents are big.
   (b) Parents sleep a lot.
   (c) Lots of families have mums and dads who work.
   (d) Parents don't know how to do the jobs.

   The best answer is ☐.

2. *Write three jobs from paragraph 3 which children can do to help.*

   - _____

   - _____

   - _____

3. *Complete the sentence. (Paragraph 5)*

   'When children are useful at home, it reminds them that they

   are _____

   _____.'

Remember:

- The main idea joins all the other ideas together. It tells what the text is mainly about.

- The title gives a clue about the main idea.

- Check all possible answers before choosing one.

Name: _____ Date: _____

1. *The main idea of the whole text is:*

   (a) Children are clever.

   (b) Children should help at home.

   (c) Children are busy people.

   (d) Children are always naughty.

   The best answer is ☐.

2. *Write the number of the paragraph which tells:*

   (a) Parents are busy and need children to help. ☐

   (b) Children can do little jobs to help. ☐

   (c) Doing jobs teaches children to be responsible. ☐

   (d) Doing jobs helps children to feel good about themselves. ☐

   (e) Doing jobs helps children to be more active. ☐

Teachers notes – 1

The focus of this section is on the following skills:

Sequencing	Finding similarities and differences	Predicting

Sequencing

Objective

• Pupils will sequence events.

Background information

This section demonstrates how to determine the order in which events occur, sometimes using time markers and other strategies to identify the relationship between events.

Knowing the sequence of events is an important, often critical, factor in a reader's understanding of a text.

Firstly, pupils need to determine from the question which events they are required to sequence. Then, they should locate them in the text and look for any time markers that could be helpful. Examples could include *before, then, when, while, after, finally, at last* or *following*.

Pupils may also find creating time lines of sections of the text or specific events a useful strategy.

Answers

I jump out of bed ....Pages 28–31

• *Practice page*: Page 30
1. (b)   2. (c)   3. (c)   4. (d)
• *On your own*: Page 31
1. (a)   2. (b)   3. 8, 6, 4, 2, 3, 1, 5, 7
4. Teacher check

How to make fairy bread ....Pages 32–33

• *Try it out*: Page 33
1. (d)   2. (b)
3. (a) Use the knife to butter the slices of bread.
   (b) Cut the fairy bread into triangles.

Finding similarities and differences

Objective

• Pupils will compare and contrast people, places and events.

Background information

The ability to compare and contrast the information provided in a text enhances the reader's understanding of that text and is an important comprehension skill pupils need to practise.

Pupils are required to categorise information to determine what some people, places and events have in common, or how they differ.

Graphic organisers are a very useful tool for identifying similarities and differences, particularly Venn diagrams, T–charts and compare and contrast charts.

same	different

T-chart

A	B	A	B
compare		contrast	

Compare and contrast chart

Answers

My family ....Pages 34–37

• *Practice page*: Page 36
1. (a)   2. (b)   3. (c)   4. (d)
5. Mum and 'me'
• *On your own*: Page 37
1. (b)   2. (d)
3. (a) True   (b) False   (c) False   (d) True   (e) False
4. Dad — make things;
   Mum — walk/garden;
   Gran — go to gym/bowl/go on bus trips;
   Steve — boss younger sister;
   'me' — do puzzles

My favourite places ....Pages 38–39

• *Try it out*: Page 39
1. (c)   2. (c)
3. Teacher check
4. Teacher check

Teachers notes – 2

Predicting

Objective

- Pupils will use information from a text to predict outcomes not explicitly stated in the text.

Background information

To be able to predict outcomes, often in terms of the probable actions or reactions of specific characters, pupils need to focus on content and to understand what they read. They need to monitor their understanding as they read, constantly confirming, rejecting or adjusting their predictions.

The focus of this section is on teaching pupils how to locate and use the information provided in the text to determine probable outcomes and then to evaluate their predictions.

Pupils need to be able to locate specific information related to an issue and/or characters using keywords and concepts. Their predictions should not be wild guesses, but well thought out, logical ideas based on the information provided and some prior knowledge.

If pupils' answers differ, it is suggested that they check again to see why their answer varies from the one given. If they can justify their answer, teachers may decide to accept it.

Answers

The man and the singing bird .... Pages 40–43

- *Practice page*: Page 42
  1. (b)   2. Teacher check   3. (a)
- *On your own*: Page 43
  1. (d)   2. (c)   3. Teacher check

The lion and the dolphin .... Pages 44–45

- *Try it out*: Page 45
  1. (c)
  2. Pupils could have ticked (a), (c) and (d) but other answers may be acceptable as long as pupils can justify their answer.
  3. Teacher check

Pupil tests

Tests have been incorporated to provide teachers with a clear record of each pupil's level of understanding and development pertaining to each skill.

A class test record sheet is provided on page viii and an individual pupil evaluation sheet on page ix.

The chatting elf

- **Test 1 — Sequencing** .... Page 47
  1. (d)
  2. (b)
  3. 3, 4, 1, 2

- **Test 2 — Finding similarities and differences** .... Page 48
  1. (c)
  2. (a)

	Morning	Lunch	Afternoon
Bill and Bob			✓
Mrs Snout	✓		
Mrs Snoop		✓	
Mr Cream	✓		

  (b) Mrs Snout and Mr Cream

- **Test 3 — Predicting** .... Page 49
  1. (d)
  2. Teacher check

Sequencing is the order in which events happen. Sequencing helps you to understand what you read.

I jump out of bed

First, I jump out of bed in the morning.

I jump out of bed in the morning.

I jump out of bed in the morning

Then I tidy the bedclothes.

Next, I eat breakfast in the morning.

I eat breakfast in the morning.

I eat breakfast in the morning

Then I rinse my dishes.

Then I clean my teeth in the morning.

I clean my teeth in the morning.

I clean my teeth in the morning.

Then I get dressed in my school clothes.

Then I pack my school bag in the morning.

I pack my school bag in the morning.

I pack my school bag in the morning.

Finally, I walk to school.

Sequencing

Learning about the skill

Learn how to work out the sequence of events.

> Remember: Order is very important.
>
> - Ask 'Which events need to be sequenced?'
>
> - Find the events and underline them.
>
> - Work out how these events fit together. Look for time marker words like *then, before, next* etc.
>
> - Check ALL the answers before deciding.

1. *Read the question.*

   What happens first in the morning?

   (a) I tidy the bedclothes. (b) I yawn.

   (c) I stretch. (d) I jump out of bed.

2. *The important word in the question is **first**. Underline it.*

3. *Find the word **first** in the text. Underline it. (**First** is a time marker word.)*

   First means the part of the text you are looking for comes **before** other parts of the text.

4. *Choosing the best answer.*

   (a) The child does tidy the bedclothes but it is not the first thing done. It does not come in first position in the text. It is the second thing the child does. This is not the best answer.

   (b) The text does not tell us that the child yawned. This is not a good answer.

   (c) The text does not tell us that the child stretched. This is not a good answer.

   (d) 'I jump out of bed' comes first in the text and follows the word **first** (a time marker word). This is the best answer.

Sequencing

Practise sequencing. (Clues are given to help you.)

1. **What does the child do after eating breakfast?**

   (a) jump out of bed   (b) rinse the dishes

   (c) clean the kitchen   (d) read a book

   The best answer is ⬚.

   > **Think!**
   > Find 'eat breakfast' in the text and see what comes **after** it.

2. **What was the next thing to happen after the child rinsed his/her dishes?**

   (a) I watch television.   (b) I go to school.

   (c) I clean my teeth.   (d) The family had lunch.

   The best answer is ⬚.

   > **Think!**
   > Find the words 'Then I rinse my dishes', then read the very **next** event.

3. **What does the child do before eating breakfast?**

   (a) schoolwork   (b) clean his/her teeth

   (c) tidy the bedclothes   (d) play a game

   The best answer is ⬚.

   > **Think!**
   > Some of the answers are silly. Read the others carefully and choose.

4. **Tick the final (last) thing that the child does.**

   (a) go to sleep ⬚

   (b) have a bath ⬚

   (c) pack his/her school bag ⬚

   (d) walk to school ⬚

   > **Think!**
   > Look for a bigger word with **final** in it. The answer is near the word.

Sequencing

Work out these answers.

1. What did the child do just before getting dressed in his/her school clothes?

    (a) clean his/her teeth   (b) rinse his/her dishes

    (c) walk to school   (d) play with a toy

    The best answer is ☐.

2. Just before the child walked to school, he/she ...

    (a) ate breakfast   (b) packed his/her school bag

    (c) fell asleep   (d) had a bath

    The best answer is ☐.

3. Number the events in the correct order from 1 to 8.

    (a) walk to school ☐   (b) get dressed ☐

    (c) rinse dishes   ☐   (d) tidy bed clothes ☐

    (e) eat breakfast   ☐   (f) jump out of bed ☐

    (g) clean teeth   ☐   (h) pack school bag ☐

4. Write steps in order to show what you do to get ready for school.

    [blank box]

How to make fairy bread

Fairy bread is easy to make.

Make some for a party or special snack.

You will need:

- a breadboard
- a plate
- a knife
- slices of bread
- butter or margarine
- coloured sprinkles

Steps:

1. First, put the slices of bread on the breadboard.

2. Then, use the knife to butter the slices of bread.

3. Next, shake coloured sprinkles onto the buttered bread.

4. Then, cut the fairy bread into triangles.

5. Finally, place the fairy bread on a plate to serve.

Test:

Eat and enjoy!

Sequencing

Use the strategies you learnt and practised in
I jump out of bed to work out the sequence.

Remember: Order is very important.

- Ask 'Which events need to be sequenced?'

- Find the events in the text and underline them.

- Work out how these events fit together. Look for time marker words like *then, before, next* etc.

- Check ALL the answers before deciding.

1. *What should you do first?*

    (a) Cut up the bread.   (b) Eat the fairy bread.

    (c) Butter the bread.   (d) Put the slices of bread on the breadboard.

    The best answer is ☐.

> **Think!**
> Find the answers in the text. Work out which one comes first.

2. *What is the last (final) step?*

    (a) Cut the fairy bread into triangles.

    (b) Place the fairy bread onto a plate to serve.

    (c) Shake on the sprinkles.

    (d) Butter the bread.

    The best answer is ☐.

3. *Write the next step after each of the ones below.*

    (a) Put the slices of bread on the breadboard.

    _____

    (b) Shake coloured sprinkles onto the buttered bread.

    _____

Finding similarities and differences – 1

Finding out how things are similar or different can help you understand what you read.

Read the table which tells about a family.

My family	Dad	Mum	Gran	Steve	me
What they look like	tall black hair brown eyes skinny very fit	tall black hair brown eyes cuddly	old short grey hair brown eyes	tall brown eyes black hair	young short cuddly brown eyes brown hair
The job they do	cameraman for a television station	sell dresses in a dress shop	clean house babysit	go to school help at home	go to school help at home
What they like to do	read run make things	walk read garden	go to gym play cards bowl go on bus trips	boss younger sister run	read play cards run do puzzles
What they like to wear	jeans and a shirt	nice dresses	pink tracksuit	tracksuit and running shoes	shorts and T-shirt

Finding similarities and differences

Learn how to organise information to make it easy to answer questions about similarities and differences.

> Remember:
>
> • What is the question asking for? Underline the keywords.
>
> • A table or chart can help to see similarities and differences.
>
> • Check all answers before deciding.

1. *Read the question.*

   Which three people in the family are tall?

   (a) Mum and Dad   (b) Gran and 'me'

   (c) Gran, Steve and 'me'   (d) Dad, Mum and Steve

2. *Underline the key words **three** and **tall** in the question. This is the important information to look for about the people. You need to find three people who are tall.*

3. *Choosing the best answer.*

   (a) Dad and Mum are tall. This may be a good answer, but the question asks for **three** people. There are only two people in this answer. So this is not a good answer.

   (b) Gran and 'me' are short. There are also only **two** people. The question asks for **three** people. This is not a good answer.

   (c) There are **three** people in this answer so this could be the best one. In the table, Steve is tall but Gran is short and so is 'me'. This is not the best answer.

   (d) There are **three** people in this answer so this could be the best answer but we need to check in the table. Dad is tall, Mum is tall and Steve is tall. This is the best answer.

Finding similarities and differences

Practice page

Practise finding similarities and differences.
(Clues are given to help you.)

1. Which three people have black hair?

    (a) Dad, Mum and Steve   (b) Steve and 'me'

    (c) Gran and Mum   (d) Mum, Gran and Steve

    The best answer is ☐.

    Think! Find answers with three people. Read the table.

2. Which two people are short?

    (a) Dad and Steve   (b) Gran and 'me'

    (c) Mum and Gran   (d) Gran and Steve

    The best answer is ☐.

    Think! There are two people in each answer. Look for the word **short** in the table.

3. Who likes to play cards?

    (a) Dad   (b) Mum   (c) Gran and 'me'   (d) Steve

    The best answer is ☐.

    Think! Read the things each likes to do.

4. Three people like to run. Who are they?

    (a) Mum, Steve and 'me'   (b) Dad, Mum and Gran

    (c) Mum, Gran and Steve   (d) Dad, Steve and 'me'

    The best answer is ☐.

    Think! Find the names in the table.

5. Write the names of two cuddly people.

    _____ and _____

Finding similarities and differences

Work out these answers.

1. Which three people like to read?

    (a) Steve and 'me'   (b) Dad, Mum and 'me'

    (c) Gran and 'me'   (d) Dad, Steve and 'me' The best answer is ☐.

2. Which person is different from the others because he/she likes to wear 'dressy' clothes?

    (a) Gran   (b) Steve

    (c) Dad   (d) Mum   The best answer is ☐.

3. Circle True or False.

    (a) Everyone has brown eyes.   True   False

    (b) Everyone likes to wear sports clothes.   True   False

    (c) Everyone has black hair.   True   False

    (d) Everyone likes to exercise.   True   False

    (e) The children don't help at home.   True   False

4. Write words in the table to show one thing that each person likes to do which is different from the others.

Dad	Mum	Gran	Steve	me

My favourite places

1. My garden and my bedroom are my two favourite places.

2. In my garden, I have a playhouse, sandpit, slippery dip and a swing set.

3. I have a little patch of garden where Mum is helping me grow flowers and tomatoes.

4. I can sit on the grass and feel the warm sun on my face.

5. I play in this favourite place with Bess, my dog, and Clyde, my cat.

6. In my bedroom, I have a bed, a wardrobe and a chest of drawers. I have a bookcase and a big toy box. My toy dog and teddy bear sit on the top.

7. My bedroom has stars, planets, the sun, the moon and spaceships on the walls and ceiling. I can lie on my starry bed cover and look up at the sun or just daydream.

8. I play in this favourite place with my cars, trucks and robots on my rug.

9. My favourite places are special to me.

Finding similarities and differences

Try it out

Use the strategies you learnt and practised in
My family to work out similarities and differences.

> Remember:
>
> • What is the question asking for? Underline the keywords.
>
> • A table or chart can help to see similarities and differences.
>
> • Check all answers before deciding.

1. *The garden and the bedroom both have ...*

   (a) a slippery dip   (b) a sandpit

   (c) a sun   (d) grass

   The best answer is ☐.

> **Think!**
> Find the words in the answers in the text. Read where they are.

2. *The garden and the bedroom both have ...*

   (a) a plant   (b) a cat   (c) a dog   (d) a bed

   The best answer is ☐.

3. *Draw something in your bedroom that is ...*

   (a) the same as in this bedroom.   (b) different from this bedroom.

4. *Colour the things that are different in your garden.*

playhouse	sandpit	slippery dip	dog
tomatoes	grass	flowers	cat

As we read, we need to think about what is happening and work out what we think will happen next.

─ The man and the singing bird ─

1. One night a man heard a bird singing happily.

2. The man really liked the singing. He set a trap for the bird by putting food in a cage and leaving the door open.

3. 'I've caught you now', he said. 'So you can sing for me all the time!'

4. 'I can't sing in a cage', said the bird.

5. 'If you can't sing for me,' said the man, 'I will have to kill you and eat you on toast'.

6. 'No! Please don't kill me!' cried the bird. 'Set me free and I will tell you three important things. These three things will be worth a lot more to you than eating me.'

7. The man set the bird free. He flew up onto a branch of a tree.

8. Then the bird said to the man, 'These are the three things I have to tell you:

9. 'One — Never believe something a captive bird tells you!

   Two — Keep what you have!

   Three — Don't be sad when you have lost something forever!'

10. Then the singing bird flew away.

Learning about the skill

Learn how to work out what probably happens next.

> Remember:
> - The answers are **not** in the text.
> - Find information in the text to use and think about.
> - Find and underline information which tells about the question.
> - Think hard! What is the writer saying might happen?
> - Think about all answers before deciding.

1. *What do you think the bird will probably do now he is free?*

    (a) find another man to sing for

    (b) eat toast

    (c) lay eggs

    (d) sing in a new place which is safe

2. *Choosing the best answer.*

    (a) The bird would probably have been frightened by the man. He was almost killed. He probably wouldn't find another man to sing for. This is not a good answer.

    (b) Birds do eat toast but this bird was almost put on toast and eaten by the man. Toast might remind him about how he was caught and almost eaten. This may not be the best answer.

    (c) The text says 'He flew up ...'. This tells us that the bird is not a female bird. Only female birds lay eggs. This is not a good answer.

    (d) The bird is a singing bird. He will keep on singing. But he will probably find a new, safer place to sing next time. This is the best answer.

Predicting

Practise predicting. (Clues are given to help you.)

1. How do you think the bird will feel next time he sings at night?

   (a) hungry　　　(b) happy

   (c) tired　　　　(d) sad

   The best answer is ☐.

> **Think!**
> Read the first sentence and underline the part about the bird singing.

2. Draw a picture of the kind of trap you think the man will use next time to catch a bird.

> **Think!**
> Read how the man caught the bird in the story. Think of how he might do it next time.

3. What do you think the man would do if he didn't catch the bird?

   (a) He would keep on trying.

   (b) He would make dinner.

   (c) He would go for a walk.

   (d) He would read a book.

   The best answer is ☐.

> **Think!**
> Read the first four sentences. Underline the parts that tell about the singing.

Predicting

Work out these predictions.

1. Next time people tell the man they will do something, do you think he will ...

   (a) listen carefully?

   (b) run away?

   (c) eat toast?

   (d) think they are trying to trick him?

   The best answer is ☐.

2. What do you think the bird will do if he sees a piece of toast?

   (a) sing

   (b) tell his friends

   (c) think about his lucky escape

   (d) eat it

   The best answer is ☐.

3. Draw a picture to show what you think the man will do next time he hears a bird singing at night.

The lion and the dolphin

1. Lion was walking by the sea one day when he saw Dolphin lift his head out of the water.

2. 'Hello, Dolphin!' said Lion. 'I am the king of the beasts. Do you want to be my friend? We could help each other.'

3. 'I am the king of the ocean', said Dolphin. 'I would like to be your friend. I would like to be able to help you too.'

4. Soon after, Lion had a fight with a wild bull. He asked Dolphin to help him.

5. Dolphin wanted to help him but he wasn't able to. He could not go on the land.

6. Lion was very angry.

7. 'You are not a good friend', he said. 'You said you would help me!'

Predicting

Use the strategies you learnt and practised in
The man and the singing bird to make predictions.

> Remember:
>
> • The answers are **not** in the text.
>
> • Find and underline information in the text to use and think about.
>
> • Think hard! What is the writer saying might happen?
>
> • Think about all answers before deciding.

1. *What will Dolphin probably say to Lion?*

   (a) 'I don't want to be your friend.'

   (b) 'I'm coming to help.'

   (c) 'I'd like to help but I can't go on the land.'

   (d) 'I didn't say that I wanted to be your friend.'

   The best answer is ☐.

> ***Think!***
> Read what the animals said to each other. Then choose an answer.

2. *Tick things that Lion could do to help himself.*

   (a) fight harder ☐   (b) run away ☐

   (c) bite and scratch ☐   (d) call other land animals to help ☐

3. *Draw what you think will happen next.*

The tests on pages 47 to 49 will show how well you can:

- **Sequence**
- **Find similarities and differences**
- **Predict**

The chatting elf

1. Once upon a time in the land of Nod, there lived an elf called Jabber who liked to chatter to everyone he met.

2. First he chatted to Mr Cream, the milkman, who was delivering his milk when the sun was coming up. Mr Cream was late delivering his milk.

3. Next he chatted to Mrs Stout when she was hanging out her big basket of washing after breakfast. Mrs Stout was late for her visit to the doctor.

4. Then he chatted to Mrs Snoop for a long time when she poked her head over the fence at lunchtime to ask him to pick up her post. Mrs Snoop was late for her visit to the hairdresser.

5. Finally, he chatted to Bill and Bob for a long time when they walked home from elf school in the afternoon. They were late getting home and their Mum was cross.

6. They thought of a plan to stop Jabber chatting so much. First, Mr Cream woke Jabber up to chat very, very early in the morning. Next, Mrs Stout chatted to him when he wanted to go shopping. The shop shut before he could do his shopping. Then Mrs Snoop chatted when he was cooking dinner and his dinner burned. Finally, Bill and Bob chatted when he wanted to take his dog for a walk. Barkey got angry and bit him.

7. Jabber decided to stop chatting so much. Now Jabber just waves to everyone as they pass his house.

Remember:

- Ask 'Which events need to be sequenced?'

- Find the events and underline them.

- Work out how these events fit together. Look for time marker words like *then, before, next* etc.

- Check ALL the answers before deciding.

Name: _____ Date: _____

1. *What did Jabber do first in the morning?*

    (a) He chatted to Bill and Bob.　　(b) He went to bed.

    (c) He cooked dinner.　　　　　　　(d) He chatted to Mr Cream.

    The best answer is ☐.

2. *Who chatted to Jabber last (finally)?*

    (a) Mrs Stout　　(b) Bill and Bob　　(c) the shopkeeper　　(d) Barkey

    The best answer is ☐.

3. *Number the events in the correct order.*

    (a) Mrs Snoop made him burn dinner.　　☐

    (b) Bill and Bob made Barkey bite him.　　☐

    (c) Mr Cream woke Jabber up.　　☐

    (d) Mrs Stout made him late for the shop.　　☐

Finding similarities and differences

Remember:

- What is the question asking for? Underline the keywords.
- A table or chart can help to see similarities and differences.
- Check all answers before deciding.

Name: _____ Date: _____

1. What same thing did Jabber cause to each person he chatted to?

   (a) He made them all burn their dinner.

   (b) He made Barkey angry at them all.

   (c) He made them all late.

   (d) He made them all late for the hairdresser.

   The best answer is ☐.

2. (a) Tick the different times of day when Jabber spoke to each person.

	Morning	Lunchtime	Afternoon
Bill and Bob			
Mrs Stout			
Mrs Snoop			
Mr Cream			

   (b) Who did he chat to at the same time of the day?

   _____ and _____

Remember:

- The answers are **not** in the text.

- Find and underline information in the text to use and think about.

- Think hard! What is the writer saying might happen?

- Think about all answers before deciding.

Name: _____ Date: _____

1. *What do you think probably would have happened if Jabber kept chatting so much?*

    (a) Jabber would go to the hairdresser.

    (b) Jabber would visit the doctor.

    (c) Barkey wouldn't get his walks.

    (d) Everyone would keep away from him.

    The best answer is ☐.

2. *Write sentences to tell what probably happened when ...*

    (a) Mrs Stout was late for her visit to the doctor.

    _____

    _____

    (b) Mrs Snoop was late getting to the hairdresser.

    _____

    _____

The focus of this section is on the following skills:

Concluding	Summarising	Inferring

Concluding

Objective

- Pupils will make judgments and reach conclusions based on facts and details provided in a text.

Background information

This section demonstrates how to decide on the meaning of facts and details provided in a text and to build up evidence in order to make judgments and reach conclusions about this information.

Pupils also need to be able to search for evidence to support a particular conclusion by locating the relevant information in the text, and then making judgments about it.

In higher order comprehension skills such as this, answers are not always immediately obvious and discussion about why one answer is judged to be the best should be encouraged. However, teachers may decide to accept another answer, if a pupil can provide the necessary evidence to support the answer he or she has given.

Answers

Boys ....Pages 52–55

- *Practice page*: Page 54
  1. (b)   2. (c)
  3. Teacher check: Drawings should include tall, big hands and feet, freckles, spots, spiky hair, bumps and scrapes on legs and arms, glasses, shirts hanging out.
  4. Boys don't look nice.
  5. Teacher check
  6. Answers should be similar to 'Boys don't like good things'.
- *On your own*: Page 55
  1. (b)   2. (a)
  3. These statements should be coloured:
     They push in front of you.
     They take toys off you.
     They don't see you when you want to join in.
  4. Teacher check: Drawings should include playing with trucks and trains, playing cricket or football, working or playing at school.

Dogs...Pages 56–57

- *Try it out*: Page 57
  1. (c)   2. (c)   3. (b)
  4. Teacher check: Pupils should have chosen 'Dogs are animals who make good pets.' or 'A dog would make a really great pet.'

Summarising

Objective

- Pupils will summarise text by linking important information and identifying the main points.

Background information

To be able to summarise text successfully, pupils first need to be clear about what they are being asked to do and the form their answer should take. (For example, a one-word answer or a more detailed explanation may be required.) It will help if they underline the critical words in the question.

They then need to locate any relevant information in the text, underline it and establish how it is linked. Words such as *while, but, and, when* and *as* may be significant in establishing how the information is linked. Unnecessary and irrelevant information should be omitted and the main points established for inclusion in the summary.

Pupils may need to locate information throughout the entire text in order to summarise the main points for some questions.

Answers may vary and will require teacher checking. Those given below are provided as a guide to the main points.

Answers

Strange plants...Pages 58–61

- *Practice page*: Page 60
  1. (a)
  2. Insects slip and *fall* down to the bottom of a deep *hole* in the *middle* of the pitcher plant and can't *get* out.
  3. (c)
- *On your own*: Page 61
  1. (d)   2. (a)
  3. Teacher check. Ensure all details are included.

Dentists ....Pages 62–63

- *Try it out*: Page 63
  1. (d)   2. (b)
  3. They help you look after your teeth.

The focus of this section is on the following skills:

Concluding	*Summarising*	*Inferring*

Inferring

Objective

- Pupils will make inferences about what is most likely to be true, based on information provided in the text.

Background information

Inferences are opinions about what is most likely to be true and are formed after careful evaluation of all the available facts. Pupils need to realise that because there is no information that 'tells' them the actual answer, their inferences may not be correct. They have to determine what makes the most sense, given the information provided, and to then look for details to support their decisions. They may need to use some prior knowledge to help them to determine their answer.

The focus of this section is on teaching pupils how to use contextual information, both written and visual, to determine what they believe to be true, and then to find further evidence to support their decisions.

Pupil answers will need to be teacher checked, but some possible answers have been provided as a guide.

Answers

My street ....Pages 64–67

- *Practice page*: Page 66
  1. (a) 2. (b) 3. (c)
- *On your own*: Page 67
  1. (d) 2. (c)
  3. Teacher check: Answers will be similar to 'He did not have to go to school'.
  4. Teacher check

Letter to Jack...Pages 68–69

- *Try it out*: Page 69
  1. (d) 2. (b)
  3. 'Nan and Pop are the parents of Ty's mum.' (He stayed in his Mum's old room.)
  4. Teacher check

Pupil tests

Tests have been incorporated to provide teachers with a clear record of each pupil's level of understanding and development pertaining to each skill.

A class test record sheet is provided on page viii and an individual pupil evaluation sheet on page ix.

Make fabulous fruit salad

- *Test 1 — Concluding* ....Page 71
  1. (c)
  2. (d)
  3. Teacher check
- *Test 2 — Summarising* ....Page 72
  1. (c)
  2. (a)
  3. (a) cut (b) mix (c) add
     (d) stir (e) sprinkle (f) refrigerate
  4. Teacher check
- *Test 3 — Inferring* ....Page 73
  1. (b)
  2. (c)
  3. Teacher check. Answers could include:
     (a) make it sweeter
     (b) it is cool

Concluding – 1

Conclusions are decisions we make by working something out.

We make conclusions about what we read by finding facts and details in the text and deciding what they mean.

Boys

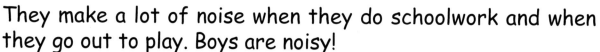

1. Boys are not nice people!

2. Boys are big. They have big feet and big hands. They get in the way because they are too tall.

3. Boys play noisy games with cars, trucks and trains. They make a lot of noise when they play cricket or football. They make a lot of noise when they do schoolwork and when they go out to play. Boys are noisy!

4. Boys are mean. When you stand in line, they try to push in front of you. Sometimes they don't even see you when you ask if you can join their game. Some boys take toys from you when you are playing with them.

5. Boys forget to put away their things. They leave rubbish behind when they eat lunch or snacks. They don't hang up their bags or coats. They don't put away their toys. They like to play in mud and sand and make a mess. Boys are messy.

6. Boys have freckles and spots and spiky hair. They have bumps and scrapes on their legs and arms. They wear glasses and do not tuck in their shirts. Boys don't look nice!

7. Boys like football, silly cartoons, bugs, fighting and books about robots. Boys don't like good things!

8. I don't think boys are nice people!

Concluding

Learning about the skill

Learn how you can work out conclusions.

Conclusions are decisions you make about the meaning of facts and details in the text.

- Find out what you are making conclusions about.

- Look in the text to find the facts and details. Underline them.

- Make decisions about what they mean.

- Check all answers before deciding.

---

1. *Read the question.*

   Why does the girl think that boys are mean?

   (a) Because boys have freckles, spots and spiky hair.

   (b) Because they play in mud and sand.

   (c) Because they like fighting.

   (d) Because they push in front of you and take your toys.

2. *You will need to find the word **mean** in paragraph 4. Underline the things she says boys do that are mean.*

3. *Choosing the best answer.*

   (a) She says boys have freckles, spots and spiky hair. But this is not why she thinks they are mean. This is not a good answer.

   (b) She says they play in mud and sand. But this is not why she thinks they are mean. This is not a good answer.

   (c) She says they fight. Fighting is a mean thing to do. But is this the best answer? You must check all answers.

   (d) In paragraph 4 she says boys are mean because they push in front of you and take your toys. This is the best answer.

Practice page

Practise concluding. (Clues are given to help you.)

1. *Why does the girl think that boys get in the way?*

   (a) Because they push you.

   (b) Because they are too tall.

   (c) Because they eat your lunch.

   (d) Because they have big hands and feet.

   The best answer is ☐.

   > **Think!**
   > Read paragraph 2. Underline why they get in the way.

2. *The girl says that boys don't like good things. She says this is because ...*

   (a) they like quiet games.

   (b) they like trucks and trains.

   (c) they like silly cartoons and books about robots.

   (d) they like being neat.

   The best answer is ☐.

   > **Think!**
   > Read paragraph 7. Underline the things boys like.

3. *Draw a picture to show why the girl thinks boys don't look nice.*

   > **Think!**
   > Read paragraph 6.

Concluding

Work out these answers.

1. *Does the girl like boys?*

    (a) yes   (b) no   (c) don't know   (d) sometimes

    The best answer is ☐.

2. *Because boys leave rubbish behind and don't put away their toys, the girl thinks they are …*

    (a) messy   (b) mean   (c) noisy   (d) silly

    The best answer is ☐.

3. *Colour the boxes that say why the girl thinks boys are mean.*

They push in front of you.	They have big feet.	They take toys off you.
They play in the mud.	They don't see you when you want to join in.	They play noisy games.

4. *Draw a picture to show why the girl thinks boys are noisy.*

Dogs

Dogs are animals who make good pets.

You need to find out what kind to get!

Some are big and some are small.

Just choose the breed you like — that's all!

Dogs don't need a lot of care.

A bed, a lead, a brush for their hair.

Some food and water and a walk.

A ball or toy and someone to talk.

Dogs wag their tail and lick your face.

They follow you all over the place.

Dogs give people so much love.

That is something I'm very sure of!

A dog would make a really great pet.

Have you decided to get one yet?

Concluding

Try it out

Use the strategies you learnt and practised in *Boys*.

Conclusions are decisions you make about the meaning of facts and details in the text.

- Find what you are making conclusions about.

- Look in the text to find the facts and details. Underline them.

- Make decisions about what they mean.

- Check all answers before deciding.

---

1. *Why does the writer conclude that dogs love people?*

   Think!
   Find the word 'love' in verse 3.

   (a) They will go for walks.

   (b) They like food.

   (c) They wag their tails and follow you.

   (d) They are good pets.   The best answer is ☐.

2. *The best conclusion for verse 2 would be ...*

   (a) Dogs bark a lot.

   (b) Dogs don't take up very much space.

   (c) Dogs don't need a lot of care.

   (d) Dogs have fleas.   The best answer is ☐.

3. *Which conclusion would be the best one for verse 1?*

   (a) Dogs are clever.

   (b) There are lots of different dogs to choose.

   (c) Dogs are big.

   (d) Dogs don't need a lot of care.   The best answer is ☐.

4. *Find and copy one sentence which would be a good conclusion for the whole poem.*

Summarising is giving the main ideas or facts without using many words. Summarising can help us to understand text.

Strange plants

1. A pitcher plant is a meat-eating plant — a carnivore! These plants eat lots of insects that get trapped in them.

2. Pitcher plants can have lovely colours. They can have nice smells. They can have sticky nectar. These attract insects to them.

3. Pitcher plants have a deep hole in the middle like a cup. When insects are trapped inside the plants, they slip on the walls and fall down to the bottom. They cannot get out.

4. Pitcher plants have a pool of special water at the bottom. When the insects fall into the water, they drown. The water 'eats' the insects. It takes two or three days to do this.

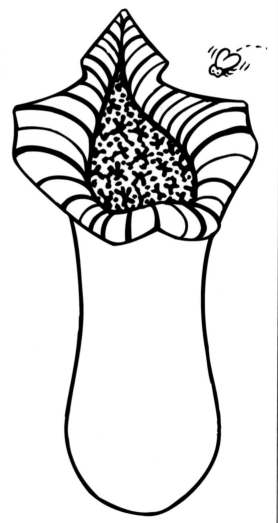

5. Pitcher plants grow in poor soil where other plants cannot grow. They cannot get food from the soil so they catch their own food to eat.

6. Pitcher plants can grow by climbing up trees. They can grow on the ground in forests. They can grow by attaching themselves to trees.

7. Pitcher plants are clever but strange plants.

Summarising

Learn how to work out the main points and summarise text.

- Make sure you understand the question. Underline the keywords.

- Look for information in the text. Decide what is important and how it is connected.

- Leave out any information you don't need.

- Check all the answers before deciding.

1. *Read the question.*

   Which sentence best summarises paragraph 1?

   (a) Pitcher plants eat meat.

   (b) Pitcher plants trap insects.

   (c) Pitcher plants eat insects.

   (d) Pitcher plants are meat-eating plants that trap insects.

2. *The keywords in the question are **best summarises**. Underline that part of the question. Read the first paragraph and underline the keywords in each sentence. Decide which information would not be needed in the summary.*

3. *Choosing the best answer.*

   (a) It does say this in paragraph 1. But important information has been left out. This is not a good answer.

   (b) It does say this in paragraph 1. But important information has been left out. This is not a good answer.

   (c) It does say this in paragraph 1. But important information has been left out. This is not a good answer.

   (d) This sentence gives **all** the important information. It is the best answer.

Summarising

Practise summarising. (Clues are given to help you.)

1. Which sentence best summarises the information in paragraph 2?

   (a) Pitcher plants use different ways to attract insects.

   (b) Pitcher plants are pretty.

   (c) Pitcher plants have to catch their own food.

   (d) Pitcher plants get food from the soil.

   The best answer is ☐.

> **Think!**
> Read paragraph 2 carefully and decide what it is telling about.

2. Complete the summary of paragraph 3.

   Insects slip and _____ down to the

   bottom of a deep _____ in the

   _____ of the pitcher plant and can't

   _____ out.

> **Think!**
> Read paragraph 3 carefully and think about the words.

3. Tick the box which gives the best summary about paragraph 4.

   (a) Pitcher plants collect water. ☐

   (b) Pitcher plants like to eat spiders. ☐

   (c) Special water in pitcher plants 'eats' insects. ☐

   (d) Insects like pitcher plants. ☐

> **Think!**
> Read paragraph 4 carefully. Find some keywords. Underline them.

Summarising

Work out these answers.

1. *Which sentence summarises paragraph 5 best?*

   (a) Pitcher plants are very hungry plants.

   (b) Pitcher plants have spines.

   (c) Pitcher plants have a 'cup' in the middle.

   (d) Pitcher plants need to catch their own food.

   The best answer is ☐.

2. *Tick the best answer. Paragraph 6 gives information about ...*

   (a) where and how pitcher plants grow ☐

   (b) what pitcher plants look like ☐

   (c) how pitcher plants make seeds ☐

   (d) the parts of a pitcher plant ☐

3. *Draw and label a diagram which summarises how pitcher plants eat. Use details from the text.*

Dentists

1. Dentists have a very important job. They help you look after your teeth.

2. Dentists have to look at your teeth, mouth and gums. If something is wrong, they work out what to do about it.

3. Dentists fill holes in teeth. They can make teeth straight. They take X-rays of teeth. They fix broken teeth. Dentists take out teeth. They order false teeth. They put fluoride on teeth to make them strong.

4. Dentists tell people what food to eat for strong, healthy teeth. They show people how to brush and floss and look after their teeth.

5. Dentists give injections or gas to keep their patients comfortable. They can also give drugs to help people with infections or pain.

6. Dentists use lots of things such as X-ray machines, drills, mouth mirrors, probes, brushes and needles. They must wear gloves and masks to protect themselves and their patients from infections.

Summarising

Try it out

Use the strategies you learnt and practised in *Strange plants* to summarise information.

Remember:

- Make sure you understand the question. Underline the keywords.

- Look for information in the text. Decide what is important and how it is connected.

- Leave out any information you don't need.

- Check all the answers before deciding.

1. **Which is the best summary of paragraph 4?**

    (a) Dentists make a lot of money.

    (b) Dentists are friendly people.

    (c) Dentists use lots of equipment.

    (d) Dentists tell you how to keep your teeth healthy.

    The best answer is ☐.

    Think!
    Read paragraph 4 carefully. There are words in the text to help you.

2. **Tick the best answer. Paragraph 6 tells about ...**

    (a) different things that can go wrong with teeth. ☐

    (b) different things that dentists use. ☐

    (c) different ways dentists fix teeth. ☐

    (d) how to look after your teeth. ☐

3. **Why do you think dentists have an important job?**

    _____

    _____

When we read, we often decide what we think might be true based on information in the text. This is called inferring.

My street

1. On Monday morning, I walked down my street with Mum to school. I met my friends at school. We learnt lots of things and played games.

2. On Monday afternoon, I walked back up the street to go home.

3. On Tuesday morning, I walked down my street to school.

4. On Tuesday afternoon, I drove up my street to go to piano lessons.

5. On Wednesday morning, I ran down my street to school. We had to hurry.

6. On Wednesday afternoon, I walked up my street to go to Brock's house to play.

7. On Thursday morning, I walked down my street to school. We learnt lots of things and sang songs.

8. On Thursday night, we drove up my street to go shopping. We ate takeaway in the food hall.

9. On Friday morning, we could walk slowly to school. We looked at the new house being built and the nice gardens.

10. On Friday night, I stayed up late and watched a film.

11. I didn't walk down my street on Saturday and Sunday.

Inferring

Learning about the skill

Learn how to work out what is most likely to be true.

- The answers are usually not in the text, but there is information to give you clues to think about. (This could be underlined.)

- Find the answer that makes the most sense and is helped by details from the text.

- Consider all answers before deciding.

---

1. *Read the question.*

    Why did the child walk to school with his mum?

    (a) He liked walking and talking with his friends.

    (b) He wanted to stretch his new shoes.

    (c) His mum wanted to get some exercise.

    (d) His mum wanted him to get to school safely.

2. *The question asks about walking to school with an adult. Think about why adults would want to walk to school with their children.*

3. *Choosing the best answer.*

    (a) The child met his friends at school. They did not walk with him and his mum to school. This is not the best answer.

    (b) This answer talks about new shoes. New shoes are not talked about at all in the text. This is not a good answer.

    (c) Lots of mums like to exercise so this may be true. This may be a good answer, but remember to read **all** of them as there may be a better answer.

    (d) Keeping children safe is very important to mums and dads. This child is probably not old enough to walk to school by himself. This is probably the best answer.

Practice page

Practise inferring. (Clues are given to help you.)

1. *Why do you think they drove to piano lessons?*

   (a) It was too far to walk.

   (b) The car engine needed to be used.

   (c) They had to carry the piano in the car.

   (d) They liked using the car to go everywhere.

   The best answer is ☐.

   > **Think!**
   > Read and think about all the answers.

2. *Where was the food hall where they ate on Thursday night?*

   (a) a long way from the shops

   (b) at the shopping centre

   (c) at their house

   (d) next to the school

   The best answer is ☐.

   > **Think!**
   > Find the words 'food hall' and read about what they did on Thursday night.

3. *Why do you think they ran to school on Wednesday morning?*

   (a) They wanted to get fit.

   (b) They liked running.

   (c) They were late.

   (d) They had new running shoes to try.

   The best answer is ☐.

   > **Think!**
   > Read paragraph 5. Then think why people have to hurry to places.

Inferring

Work out these answers.

1. *Why could they have had the time on Friday morning to look at the new house being built and the nice gardens?*

    (a) They were late for school.

    (b) They had to get up early to go to piano lessons.

    (c) They had to go to Brock's house.

    (d) They were ready for school early.

    The best answer is ☐.

2. *Why do you think the child was able to stay up late on Friday night?*

    (a) There was a good film on television.

    (b) His friends came to his house.

    (c) He did not have to get up to go to school the next day.

    (d) He did not sleep well on Friday nights.

    The best answer is ☐.

3. *Write a sentence to tell why you think the child did not walk down his street on Saturday and Sunday.*

    _____

    _____

4. *Think about what the child does at school. Draw a picture to show how you think he feels about school.*

Letter to Jack

Dear Jack,

1. It was 9 o'clock in the morning when Nan and Pop picked me up from the airport. They hugged and kissed me.

2. We climbed in the old truck and drove out of town. The road was covered with red dust. Stumpy bushes grew along the side of the road. I saw brown rabbits hopping along, and cattle standing around. The sky was as blue as the sea. There wasn't one cloud in the sky.

3. Finally, we turned onto a gravel track and drove through a set of wide gates. Two big posts stood on each side. The large sign across the posts said 'Red Farm Station'.

4. We parked the truck in the shed next to the tractor and went into the house. Pop put my suitcase in Mum's old bedroom. In the kitchen, Nan poured tall glasses of lemonade and put out a big plate of scones with jam and cream.

5. Yobbo sniffed around my feet looking for scraps while I ate my snack.

6. While Nan washed the dishes and put away the leftovers, I gazed out the window at the horses.

7. This holiday is going to be so much fun! Wish you were here, Jack. I guess I'll have to eat all Nan's great cooking all by myself.

Love

Ty

Inferring

Use the strategies you learnt and practised in *My street*.

Remember:

- The answers are usually not in the text, but there is information to give you clues to think about. (This could be underlined.)

- Find the answer that makes the most sense and is helped by details from the text.

- Consider all answers before deciding.

---

1. *Where do you think Ty's Nan and Pop live?*

   (a) near the beach   (b) in the mountains

   (c) in the city   (d) in a dry area

   The best answer is ☐.

   > **Think!**
   > Read paragraph 2.

2. *Red Farm Station is ...*

   (a) a train station   (b) a cattle station

   (c) a petrol station   (d) a fire station

   The best answer is ☐.

3. *Whose mum and dad are Nan and Pop?*

   _____

4. *Draw a picture of Red Farm Station.*

The tests on pages 71 to 73 will show how well you can:

- **Conclude**
- **Summarise**
- **Infer**

Make fabulous fruit salad

You will need:

- 1 green apple
- 1 mango
- 3 slices rockmelon
- 1 punnet strawberries
- $\frac{1}{2}$ tin pineapple pieces with juice
- bowl
- spoon

- 1 red apple
- 1 peach
- mint sprigs
- sugar to taste

- knife
- cutting board

Steps:

(a) Cut all the fruit except the pineapple into small pieces.

(b) Mix together carefully in bowl.

(c) Add mint sprigs and pineapple pieces with juice.

(d) Stir together gently.

(e) Sprinkle lightly with sugar.

(f) Refrigerate until cool.

Test:

Enjoy on a hot summer day.

Remember:

- Decide what it is you are making conclusions about.

- Look in the text to find the facts and details. Underline them.

- Make decisions about what they mean.

- Check all the answers before deciding.

Name: _____ Date: _____

1. *Why does the fruit need to be cut up?*

    (a) to make it taste better   (b) to make it easy to cook

    (c) to make it easy to eat   (d) to peel it

    The best answer is ☐.

2. *Sugar is added ...*

    (a) to look good   (b) to make it cold

    (c) to add colour   (d) to make it sweet

    The best answer is ☐.

3. *Write 'yes' or 'no'.*

    (a) The ingredients are hard to find.   _____

    (b) This recipe is hard to make.   _____

    (c) This would make a lot of fruit salad.   _____

    (d) This fruit salad would be colourful.   _____

    (e) I would like this fruit salad.   _____

Summarising

Remember:

- Make sure you understand the question. Underline the keywords.
- Look for information in the text. Decide what is important and how it is connected.
- Leave out any information you don't need.
- Check all the answers before deciding.

Name: _____ Date: _____

1. *Which word best summarises all the things which go into the fruit salad?*

   (a) cereal   (b) spices   (c) fruit   (d) meat

   The best answer is ☐.

2. *Which word best summarises all the other things which are needed to make the fruit salad?*

   (a) utensils   (b) food   (c) animals   (d) books

   The best answer is ☐.

3. *Copy words from the text to summarise the steps taken to make fruit salad.*

   (a) c_____   (b) m_____   (c) a_____

   (d) st_____   (e) sp_____   (f) r_____

4. *Complete the sentence.*

   I think fruit salad is _____.

Remember:

- The answers are usually not in the text, but there is information to give you clues to think about. (This could be underlined.)

- Find the answer that makes the most sense and is helped by details from the text.

- Check all the answers before deciding.

Name: _____ Date: _____

1. *What could the fruit be put on while it is being cut up?*

   (a) bowl   (b) cutting board   (c) spoon   (d) mat

   The best answer is ☐.

2. *What is the fruit mixed and stirred with?*

   (a) knife   (b) cutting board   (c) spoon   (d) fork

   The best answer is ☐.

3. *Complete the sentences.*

   (a) The fruit salad can be sprinkled with sugar to

   _____

   _____

   (b) The fruit salad would be good to enjoy on a hot summer

   day because _____

   _____.

Teachers notes – 1

The focus of this section is on the following skills:

Cause and effect	Fact or opinion	Point of view and purpose

Cause and effect

Objective

• Pupils will determine cause and effect and understand how they are connected.

Background information

Pupils need to understand that the *cause* leads to the *effect* and that they are connected.

This section demonstrates strategies for pupils to use in order to find information in text which, in turn, helps them to make the connection and determine cause and effect.

They need to find and underline the keywords in questions, then search for information in the text which makes connections between the keywords and either the cause or the effect. They need to understand that they will be given one in the question, but they will need to search for the other.

Answers

One to five .... Pages 76–79

• *Practice page*: Page 78
1. (a)   2. (b)
3. (a) effect   (b) cause   (c) effect
   (d) cause   (e) effect   (f) cause
• *On your own*: Page 79
1. (c)   2. (c)
3. (a) ... she fell down on the floor
   (b) ... bees from a hive tried to eat him alive

The sandman .... Pages 80–81

• *Try it out*: Page 81
1. (a)   2. (b)
3. (a) holds an umbrella with pictures on it over them
   (b) holds an umbrella over them which has no pictures on it

Fact or opinion

Objective

• Pupils will demonstrate their ability to identify facts and opinions and their understanding of how they differ.

Background information

A fact is something that is true. It can be verified by referring to other information. In other words, it can be checked and be shown to be correct.

An opinion is something that someone *believes* to be true, but which cannot be verified. In other words, it is something that someone *thinks* rather than *knows* is true.

Pupils must to be able to distinguish between facts and opinions to become critical readers. They have to engage and interact with text and read with a questioning attitude. They can then look for relationships and critically judge and evaluate what they read.

Critical readers become more discriminating consumers of the news media and advertising.

Answers

Houses .... Pages 82–85

• *Practice page*: Page 84
1. (a)   2. (b)
3. (a) fact   (b) opinion
• *On your own*: Page 85
1. (c)   2. (d)
3. (a) fact   (b) opinion   (c) fact

Showbags .... Pages 86–87

• *Try it out*: Page 87
1. (a)   2. (d)   3. opinion

The focus of this section is on the following skills:

| Cause and effect | Fact or opinion | Point of view and purpose |

Point of view and purpose

Objective

- Pupils will understand and identify the writer's point of view and purpose.

Background information

The author's point of view is his or her opinion about a subject. A reader should, after careful and detailed analysis of what has been written, understand and be able to identify the point of view expressed in the text.

The author's purpose for writing explains *why* the text was written. It may be to express a particular point of view, to amuse, entertain, inform, persuade, instruct, describe, record information or to explain something.

Pupils should be encouraged to try to work out how and what the writer was thinking and to use this to help them to make decisions about the writer's point of view. They should then look for details in the text to support or reject the choices they have made.

All possible choices should be considered before a final decision is made.

Answers

How jellyfish look after themselves .... pages 88–91

- *Practice page*: Page 90
  1. (a)   2. (b)   3. (c) it puts poison into its prey
- *On your own*: Page 91
  1. (b)   2. (a)
  3. because jellyfish are interesting and unusual
  4. Teacher check

Jack and the beanstalk .... Pages 92–93

- *Try it out*: Page 93
  1. (a)
  2. (a) silly   (b) brave   (d) liked
  3. (d)

Pupil tests

Tests have been incorporated to provide teachers with a clear record of each pupil's level of understanding and development pertaining to each skill. It is important that pupils work independently to complete the tests.

A class test record sheet is provided on page viii and an individual pupil evaluation sheet on page ix.

My dog, Barkly

- *Test 1 — Cause and effect* .... Page 95
  1. (a)
  2. (b)
  3. (a) ... I cried (b) barked (c) he dragged it all over the garden
- *Test 2 — Fact or opinion* .... Page 96
  1. (c)
  2. (b)
  3. (a) fact   (b) fact
- *Test 3 — Point of view and purpose* .... Page 97
  1. (b)
  2. (d)
  3. (b)

Cause and effect is when one thing (the cause) makes something else happen (the effect). Working out cause and effect will help you to understand what you read.

One to five

When Jamal was one
He learnt how to run.
When the dog took his bun
He didn't run for fun.

When Maria was two
She tripped on her shoe.
It was brand new
It was slippery and blue.

When Jai was three
He fell on his knee.
He tripped on the tree
Which he did not see.

When Su-Li was four
Her head hit the door.
She fell down on the floor
And felt very sore.

When Mario was five
He learnt how to dive.
Bees from a hive
Tried to eat him alive.

Cause and effect

Learning about the skill

Learn how to work out cause and effect.

> Remember:
>
> - The cause leads to the effect. They are joined together.
> - You will be told one and you will need to work out the other.
> - Look for keywords in the question and underline them.
> - Find words in the text that are joined to the key question words.
> - Check all answers before deciding.

1. *Read the question.*

   What caused Jamal to run?

   (a) Bees came after him.

   (b) He was in a race.

   (c) His mum was chasing him.

   (d) He chased the dog that took his bun.

2. *The keywords in the question are **Jamal** and **run**. Underline them in the question. Find the keywords in the same verse in the poem. Underline them.*

3. *Choosing the best answer.*

   (a) The bees are talked about later in the poem, but it is Mario who is chased by the bees. This is not the best answer.

   (b) The poem does not say anything about Jamal being in a race. This is not a good answer.

   (c) The poem does not say anything about Jamal's mum at all. This is not a good answer.

   (d) The first verse tells about Jamal learning to run when the dog took his bun. He did not run for fun. This is the best answer.

Cause and effect

Practise finding cause and effect.
(Clues are given to help you.)

1. **What caused Maria to trip over her shoe?**

   (a) The shoes were slippery and new.

   (b) She ran after the dog.

   (c) She did not tie her shoelace.

   (d) The shoe was too big for her.

   The best answer is ☐.

   > **Think!**
   > Find and read the verse where Maria and her shoe are talked about. The cause is in the same verse.

2. **What caused Jai to fall on his knee?**

   (a) He twisted his ankle.

   (b) He tripped on the tree.

   (c) He slipped on the floor.

   (d) He tripped over Jamal's foot.

   The best answer is ☐.

   > **Think!**
   > Find and read a verse which tells about Jai. Find the cause.

3. **Write *cause* or *effect* for each.**

   > **Think!**
   > Think about what caused something to happen.

   (a) Jamal learnt how to run ... _____

   (b) the dog took his bun. _____

   (c) Maria tripped on her shoe ... _____

   (d) her new shoe was slippery. _____

   (e) Jai fell on his knee ... _____

   (f) he tripped on the tree. _____

Cause and effect

On your own

Work out these answers.

1. **What caused Su-Li to feel very sore?**

> **Think!**
> Find and read the verse where Su-Li is talked about.

   (a) She cut her finger.

   (b) She bumped her foot.

   (c) She hit her head on the door and fell on the floor.

   (d) She tripped on her new blue shoe.

   The best answer is ☐.

2. **What caused Mario to learn to dive?**

   (a) He was swimming with his dad.

   (b) He was in a submarine.

   (c) Bees from a hive tried to eat him alive.

   (d) He tripped on a tree.

   The best answer is ☐.

3. **Copy words from the poem to write the cause to match each effect.**

   (a) Su-Li hit her head on the door because ...

   _____

   _____.

   (b) Mario learnt to dive because ...

   _____

   _____.

The sandman

1. The sandman visits children at night-time.

2. He takes off his shoes and walks in his socks so he doesn't make any noise.

3. He opens doors without making any noise.

4. He throws dust into children's eyes so that they can't open them and see him.

5. The sandman sneaks behind children and blows on their necks to make them sleepy.

6. He likes children. He only wants them to be quiet while he tells them stories.

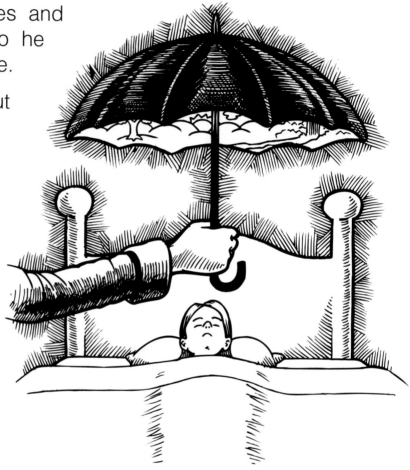

7. He holds an umbrella with pictures on it over good children. They dream beautiful stories all night.

8. He holds an umbrella with no pictures on it over bad children. They sleep all night without having any dreams.

9. In the morning the children wake up. They have to wipe sleep dust from their eyes because the sandman has paid them a visit during the night.

Cause and effect

Use the strategies you learnt and practised in *One to five* to work out cause and effect.

Remember:

- The cause leads to the effect. They are joined together.

- You will be told one. You will need to work out the other.

- Look for keywords in the question. Underline them.

- Find words in the text that are joined to the key question words.

- Check all answers before deciding.

---

1. *What is the effect of the sandman taking off his shoes and walking in his socks?*

   Think!
   Read paragraph 2.

   (a) He makes no noise.   (b) He does not slip over.

   (c) He hides the holes.   (d) His feet do not smell so much.

   The best answer is ☐.

2. *Why can't the children open their eyes?*

   (a) He glues them shut.   (b) He throws dust in their eyes.

   (c) He tapes them shut.   (d) They are very quiet.

   The best answer is ☐.

3. *Complete the sentences.*

   (a) Good children dream beautiful dreams because he ...

   _____

   (b) Bad children have no dreams because he ...

   _____

Fact or opinion – 1

When reading it is important to understand the difference between facts and opinions and to work out which is which.

A fact is something that is true.

An opinion is something that someone THINKS is true.

Houses

1. A house is a building where people live.

2. Houses have a roof and walls. Roofs can be made of grass, wood, metal, tiles or other things. A tile roof looks the best.

3. Houses can be made of brick, grass, ice, timber or other material. Brick is the best material for building houses.

4. Houses have rooms to do different things in. Some houses have many rooms. Some have only a few rooms. A house with lots of rooms would be good for a big family.

5. Houses can be big or small. Small houses are easier to look after than big houses.

6. Some houses have a garden. My big garden is good.

7. Houses like a castle or an igloo stay in one place. Houses like a caravan, boat or tent can be moved around. A house that moves would be fun to live in.

8. Houses can have a garage or a carport for cars. A house with a garage is better because you can lock it up.

9. People need houses to keep them safe from rain, wind, heat and cold.

10. I'm glad I've got my house to live in!

Fact or opinion

Learning about the skill

Learn how to work out if something is a fact or an opinion.

- Ask yourself:

  Can the statement be checked and proved to be correct? If it can, it's a fact.

  Is it what someone thinks is true and can't be proved? If so, it's an opinion.

  For example: Hens lay eggs. (fact)

  Eggs taste good. (opinion)

- Check all the answers before deciding.

---

1. *Read the question.*

   Which sentence is an opinion?

   (a) Houses have a roof and walls.

   (b) Roofs can be made of grass, wood, metal, tiles or other things.

   (c) Houses need roofs.

   (d) A tile roof looks the best.

2. *Choosing the best answer.*

   (a) This is a fact that would be easy to check in books. This is not a good answer.

   (b) This information could be checked in books or on the Internet. These are facts. This is not a good answer for the question.

   (c) This information could be checked and is a fact. This is not a good answer.

   (d) This sentence does not give information that can be checked. This is an opinion. This is the best answer.

Fact or opinion

Practise working out facts and opinions. (Clues are given to help you.)

1. **Which sentence is a fact?**

   (a) Houses can be made of brick, grass, ice, timber or other material.

   (b) Houses look nice with a garden.

   (c) All houses should be made of grass.

   (d) All houses should be made of timber.

   The best answer is ☐.

   > **Think**
   > Which ones tell what someone THINKS and cannot be checked?

2. **Which sentence is an opinion?**

   (a) Bricks are made of clay.

   (b) Brick is the best material for building houses.

   (c) Houses can be made of brick.

   (d) Bricks can be used to build walls.

   The best answer is ☐.

   > **Think**
   > Find the ones which are facts first and can be checked. The one left should be an opinion!

3. **Write 'fact' or 'opinion' for each sentence.**

   (a) Houses have rooms to do different things in.

   _____

   > **Think**
   > Read each sentence carefully and think about it.

   (b) A house with lots of rooms would be good for a big family.

   _____

Fact or opinion

Work out these answers.

1. *Which sentence is a fact?*

   (a) Small houses are easier to look after than big houses.

   (b) Small houses are cute.

   (c) Houses can be big or small.

   (d) My big garden is good.

   The best answer is ☐.

2. *Which sentence is an opinion?*

   (a) Houses like a castle or igloo stay in one place.

   (b) Houses like a caravan, boat or tent can be moved around.

   (c) A house is a building where people live.

   (d) A house that moves would be fun to live in.

   The best answer is ☐.

3. *Write 'fact' or 'opinion' below each sentence.*

   (a) Houses can have a garage or a carport for cars.

   _____

   (b) A house with a garage is better because you can lock it up.

   _____

   (c) People need houses to keep them safe from rain, wind, heat and cold.

   _____

Showbags

1. Showbags are big, colourful bags full of goodies which are sold at the show or fair. Showbags are the best things to buy at the show. Everyone who goes should buy a showbag.

2. There are lots of different kinds of showbags. Some are big. They have lots of things in them. Some are small. They only have a few things in them. I like the big ones best because you get lots of goodies. Everyone should buy big showbags.

3. Some showbags can cost a lot. Some don't cost very much at all. It is better to save up your pocket money and buy one that costs a lot because you get lots of things in it.

4. Showbags can be filled with comics, little plastic toys, sweets, drinks, games, stickers, masks, balloons and other goodies. The ones filled with chocolate and sweets are the best. Everyone should buy the showbags filled with lots of sweets and chocolates.

5. Showbags are not too heavy to carry around. You need to buy the best ones first before they are all sold. If you have enough money you can buy a few showbags to take home.

6. Everyone should buy showbags when they go to the show.

Fact or opinion

Use the strategies you learnt and practised in *Houses* to work out facts and opinions.

Remember

- A fact can be checked and proved to be correct.

- An opinion is what someone thinks is true. It can't be proved.

- Check all the answers before deciding.

---

1. *Which sentence is a fact?*

    (a) Showbags are big, colourful bags full of goodies which are sold at the show.

    (b) Showbags are the best things to buy at the show.

    (c) Everyone should buy big showbags.

    (d) Everyone who goes should buy a showbag.

    The best answer is ☐.

> **Think!**
> Which one can be proved and is a fact?

2. *Which sentence is an opinion?*

    (a) Some showbags are small.

    (b) Some showbags are big.

    (c) Some showbags can cost a lot.

    (d) It is best to buy a showbag that costs a lot.

    The best answer is ☐.

3. *Write 'fact' or 'opinion' for the sentence.*

    The ones filled with chocolate and sweets are the best.

    _____

When we read, we should try to think like the writer. Then we can try to work out how and what he or she feels and believes (the writer's point of view). We can also try to work out why he or she wrote the text (the writer's purpose).

How jellyfish look after themselves

1. Jellyfish are very unusual animals. They don't have eyes, brains, bones or a heart. They can sense light and smell things to work out where they are.

2. Jellyfish have clever ways of protecting themselves. They have bodies you can see through. This makes it easy for them to hide from animals wanting to catch and eat them. Some turtles, fish, sea snails and slugs eat jellyfish. Healthy jellyfish can grow new bits of their tentacles if they hurt them.

3. Jellyfish sting with their tentacles. They sting animals to catch and eat them. When a jellyfish stings, it puts poison into its prey. They also use their tentacles to fight other animals. Jellyfish can be dangerous for other animals to meet in the sea.

4. Jellyfish eat waterplants and tiny sea creatures. Bigger jellyfish can sometimes eat small fish and prawns. Jellyfish can be nasty because they even eat smaller jellyfish!

5. Jellyfish do not often hurt humans because they are quite shy and will try to move away. People who are hurt by jellyfish are usually stung by accident because they have disturbed a jellyfish.

Point of view and purpose

Learning about the skill

Learn how to work out the writer's point of view and his or her probable purpose or reason for writing the text.

- Writers don't always just tell you what they think or believe or why they have written the text. Sometimes you have to try to think like they do and work it out for yourself.

- In the text, there are details and information for you to find, underline and use in making your choices.

- Check all answers before deciding.

---

1. *Read the question.*

   Does the writer think that jellyfish are often dangerous to …

   (a) people?

   (b) swimmers?

   (c) birds?

   (d) small sea animals?

2. *Choosing the best answer.*

   (a) In paragraph 5 the writer says that jellyfish do not often hurt humans because they are quite shy. This is probably not the best answer.

   (b) A swimmer could disturb a jellyfish but it would try to move away. This is probably not the best answer.

   (c) The writer doesn't say anything about birds. So this is not a good answer.

   (d) The writer says that jellyfish eat tiny sea animals so jellyfish would be dangerous for them. This is the best answer.

Point of view and purpose

Practise working out what the writer believes and why he or she wrote the text. (Clues are given to help you.)

1. *The writer believes that ...*

    (a) Jellyfish can be dangerous animals.

    (b) Jellyfish are friendly animals to play with in the sea.

    (c) Jellyfish make good pets.

    (d) Jellyfish can be kept in a fish tank.

    The best answer is ☐.

> **Think!**
> Read the information in paragraph 3.

2. *The writer believes that ...*

    (a) Jellyfish are funny.

    (b) Jellyfish have a clever way of protecting themselves.

    (c) Jellyfish have no way of protecting themselves.

    (d) Jellyfish can do tricks.

    The best answer is ☐.

> **Think!**
> Read the information in paragraph 2.

3. *Complete the sentence.*

    The writer thinks that jellyfish are dangerous, because when a jellyfish stings an animal ...

    _____

    _____

> **Think!**
> Find and read a paragraph which tells about this.

Point of view and purpose

Work out these answers.

1. *The writer thinks jellyfish are **clever**, because ...*

   (a) they are good swimmers.

   (b) they can grow new bits.

   (c) they eat each other.

   (d) they sting people.

   The best answer is ☐.

2. *What does the writer think about jellyfish?*

   (a) They are interesting and unusual.

   (b) They shouldn't sting.

   (c) They should be caught.

   (d) They make good pets.

   The best answer is ☐.

3. *The writer wrote the text ...*

   (a) so people will be careful of jellyfish.

   (b) to make people frightened of jellyfish.

   (c) because jellyfish are interesting and unusual.

   (d) because he or she doesn't like jellyfish.

   The best answer is ☐.

4. *Write a sentence to tell your own point of view about jellyfish.*

   _____

   _____

Jack and the beanstalk

1. Jack and the beanstalk is a well-known fairytale.

2. It was sad that Jack and his mother were poor and had no food to eat.

3. But Jack was silly to swap the cow for magic beans.

4. I can understand why his mother got angry and threw the magic beans out the window.

5. Jack was very brave to climb up the tall beanstalk into the sky.

6. I liked the giant's rhyme when he said,

   'Fee! Fie! Foe! Fum!
   I smell the blood of an Englishman.
   Be he alive, or be he dead,
   I'll grind his bones to make my bread.'

7. The giant's wife was very brave to help him but Jack was very bad to steal the hen and the singing harp from the giant.

8. I didn't like Jack when he chopped down the beanstalk with his axe and killed the giant. The giant was only looking after his things.

9. This is a good story except when the giant gets killed, but lots of other children like gory stories.

Point of view and purpose

Use the strategies you learnt and practised in *How jellyfish look after themselves* to work out the writer's point of view and purpose.

> **Remember**
>
> • Writers don't always tell you what they think or why they have written the text. You have to try to think like they do and work it out for yourself.
>
> • In the text, there are details and information about the question to find, underline and use to make your choices.
>
> • Check all answers before deciding.

1. What does the writer think about Jack and his mother being poor?

   > **Think!**
   > Read paragraph 2.

   (a) It was sad.   (b) It was a good thing.

   (c) It was funny.   (d) It was nice.

   The best answer is ☐ .

2. Complete the sentences to show what the writer thinks.

   (a) Jack was _____ to swap the cow for beans.

   (b) Jack was _____ to climb up the beanstalk.

   (c) I _____ the giant's rhyme.

3. Do you think the writer wrote the text …

   (a) to tell the story?

   (b) because he or she was happy?

   (c) because he or she was sad?

   (d) to tell what he or she thinks about the story?

   The best answer is ☐ .

The tests on pages 95 to 97 will show how well you can work out:

- **Cause and effect**   • **Fact or opinion**   • **Point of view and purpose**

My dog, Barkly

1. Yesterday, my dog, Barkly, died at the vet's. He was a very old dog.

2. I was very sad so I cried. My brother, Max, cried too. We loved Barkly very much. He was a good dog. He was a member of our family.

3. Barkly used to dig holes in Mum's garden. She didn't like that. It made her mad. But she still loved Barkly. He had been with us since he was a pup.

4. Barkly was glad to see me when I came home from school. He wagged his tail and followed me around. I liked him doing that. He was a good friend.

5. Barkly was the best dog in the whole world. He did not bite anyone. He did not bark much unless he was excited.

6. Barkly's favourite toy was his blanket. It was dirty with holes in it. He dragged it all over the garden. We had to keep washing it and putting it back in his kennel. It looked like a rag, but he loved it.

7. Mum washed Barkly's blanket for me. I'm keeping it to remember what a good friend Barkly was.

Cause and effect

Remember:
- The cause leads to the effect. They are joined together.
- You will be told one. You will need to work out the other.
- Look for keywords in the question. Underline them.
- Find words in the text that are joined to the key question words.
- Check all answers before deciding.

Name: _____ Date: _____

1. **What caused Barkly to die?**

   (a) He was a very old dog.   (b) He ran away.

   (c) He got hit by a car.   (d) He was very sick.

   The best answer is ☐.

2. **What did Barkly do to cause Mum to get mad?**

   (a) Barkly liked to pull the washing off the line.

   (b) Barkly liked to dig holes in Mum's garden.

   (c) Barkly kept running out the gate.

   (d) Barkly liked to chew her shoes.

   The best answer is ☐.

3. **Copy words from the text to explain the effect.**

   (a) I was very sad so _____.

   (b) Barkly _____ when he was excited.

   (c) Barkly's blanket was dirty and had holes in it because

   _____

Fact or opinion

Remember

- A fact can be checked and proved to be correct.
- An opinion is what someone thinks is true and can't be proved.
- Check all the answers before deciding.

Name: _____ Date: _____

1. *Which sentence is a fact?*

   (a) Barkly was a good dog.

   (b) Barkly was the best dog in the whole world.

   (c) Barkly was a very old dog.

   (d) Barkly was a good friend.

   The best answer is ☐.

2. *Which sentence is an opinion?*

   (a) Barkly died at the vet's.

   (b) Barkly was the best dog in the whole world.

   (c) Barkly used to dig holes in Mum's garden.

   (d) Barkly was a very old dog.

   The best answer is ☐.

3. *Write 'fact' or 'opinion' for each statement.*

   (a) Barkly did not bite anyone.   _____

   (b) Barkly's favourite toy was his blanket.   _____

Point of view and purpose

- Writers don't always tell you what they think or believe or why they have written the text. Sometimes you have to work it out for yourself.

- The text has details and information to find and use in making your choices. (These could be underlined.)

- Check all answers before deciding.

Name: _____ Date: _____

1. **What does the writer think about dogs?**

   (a) They make a lot of noise.

   (b) They are good pets to have.

   (c) They are messy.

   (d) They can bite.

   The best answer is ☐.

2. **The writer thinks dogs make good pets because they ...**

   (a) drag things around.

   (b) bite people.

   (c) bark.

   (d) are like good friends.

   The best answer is ☐.

3. **Do you think the writer wrote the text because he or she ...**

   (a) was angry?   (b) wanted to tell about Barkly?

   (c) doesn't like dogs?   (d) was crying?

   The best answer is ☐.